The Open Garden

By the same author

The Enchanted Places
The Path Through the Trees
The Hollow on the Hill

CHRISTOPHER MILNE

The Open Garden

A Story with Four Essays

A Methuen Paperback

For Lesley
whose welcome to all who visit our garden is
(with the exception of a few who visit her vegetables)
as warm as my own.

A Methuen Paperback

First published in paperback in Great Britain in 1988
by Methuen London, Michelin House,
81 Fulham Road, London SW3 6RB
The Windfall first published in 1985
by Methuen London Ltd
The Windfall text copyright © Christopher Milne 1985
Essays text copyright © Christopher Milne 1988
The Windfall illustrations copyright © Kenneth Lindley 1985

Photoset by Rowland Phototypesetting Ltd,
Bury St Edmunds, Suffolk
Made and printed in Great Britain
by Cox and Wyman Ltd, Reading, Berks

British Library Cataloguing in Publication Data

Milne, Christopher
The open garden: a story with four essays
I. Title
824'.914

ISBN 0-413-40800-0

Contents

Introduction

IF YOU set off to climb Mount Everest or go on an expedition to the South Pole, it is probable that your venture will be seen as a contest, a battle between man and the forces of nature. And of course everyone hopes that you will win and return in triumph. But if instead you sail alone around the world, an undertaking that appears at first sight to call for a similar display of courage and endurance, you yourself may well not see it this way at all. 'Weren't you ever afraid?' they will ask on your return. 'Didn't you ever feel lonely?' Lonely? Afraid? No! Of course not! For you were not battling single-handed against the elements. You were no gladiator defying the cruel sea. Yours, when you came back, was no victory. You and the sea and the sky had been companions. You and they had been part of something that had contained the three of you – contained, maybe, everything else as well, everything you had left behind. But alone at sea was when you had been most conscious of not being alone.

These are the two ways of looking at the world. We are told often enough that the second is the better way of looking at our fellow humans – seeing ourselves and them as part of some larger community. Yet even this is hard enough. The United Nations? But we are not united. Even within individual nations there are divisions; and we spend most of our lives trying to outrival our neighbours. It is even harder to visualise man and nature as joint ingredients of something that contains them both. But sometimes we can manage it. And some of us manage it better than others.

I am too old to sail round the world, but I can still, when most of my fellow humans are in bed, make my way to a nearby hilltop and be alone with the sheep and the stars. I have no exciting story to tell on my return – just an experience that is difficult to describe but which can, I hope, be detected lying behind the four essays and the story that follow.

The Open Garden

THERE WAS a notice down at the bottom of the hill last week. It was leaning against the wall by the bridge and it said 'Garden Open Today'. An arrow pointed up the road. But it did not point to us.

No. Ours is not that sort of garden. I am happy to show it off to visiting friends. I am even happier if they ask me questions about it and listen to my answers. And I shall be surprised if they do not from time to time pause and exclaim 'How pretty!' But opening one's garden to the public at large is a little like showing one's flowers at a flower show or one's cat at a cat show. Both flowers and cats are judged according to certain rules, and marks are lost if the stalk or the tail is too short, the anthers or the whiskers too sparse, if the petals drop off or the fur falls out. In vain do we draw attention to certain other features – the noble nature, the intelligence – in which our cat excels. These count for nothing.

Gardens, it is true, are not judged quite so strictly. But if we hang a notice on our gate certain expectations will be aroused, expectations shaped by those gardening experts who preach to us on radio and television and in gardening books, gardening magazines and the gardening pages of our newspapers, expectations reinforced by all who hope to sell us their seeds, their plants, their tools or their chemicals. And I fear that after a few minutes spent in our garden the visitor would shake his head. Too many daisies in the lawn. Roses need proper pruning. Colours not well grouped. And *far* too many weeds. Being polite, he would not say this out loud, but I should know quite well that he was thinking it. And I would want to explain to him that I *like* daisies in my lawn. Daisies are among the loveliest flowers in the world and the lawn is the correct place for them. To see them at their best you must wait for an evening when the sun is low on the horizon and their white petals are beginning to close to show their crimson tips. Then you must lie on the grass and face the sun and with your eyes at daisy level look at them against the sunset.

All gardens are the better for a certain amount of explanation on the part of the gardener, but ours, I feel, needs more than most. 'Weeds', did you say? It depends what you mean by weeds. If you are referring to our shining cranesbill, our ivy-leaved toadflax, our birdsfoot trefoil, our common vetch, our catsears, our wall pennywort. . . . But perhaps I had better begin at the beginning. The question 'What is a weed?' can wait. The first question to answer is 'What is a garden?'

Fifty years ago I would have had no difficulty answering that question. Fifty years ago I lived with my parents at Cotchford and there we had a flower garden, a kitchen garden, a meadow and a wood. Each had its own identity and was clearly separated from the others by a fence or a hedge. So, since the kitchen garden reached us by way of the kitchen and our knowledge of vegetables began only when they were lying in the dish waiting to be eaten, 'garden' to me meant 'flower garden'; and thanks to the labours of my mother there was no doubt what that meant.

Twenty-seven years ago, when Lesley and I took possession of our own first garden, I was still in no doubt about the meaning of the word. The plot of land we had bought had previously been the walled kitchen garden of the big house below us. It contained apple trees and plum trees, soft fruit and vegetables. We moved the fruit bushes and vegetables to the far end and turned the near end into flower garden. To keep the two apart I erected a small fence which only the fruit trees were allowed to disregard, being equally welcome in either territory. I had a bare, flat (though not level) expanse of earth to work on and so I was free to dig and build and pave and grass and plant as I pleased. The result was wholly conventional, a credit to my mother's teaching, and we were very proud of it.

Embridge, however, was quite different. Here we had more

land, steeper and very far from bare. On its rough and rocky slopes apple trees and oaks, hazels and blackthorns and a whole succession of flowers from the earliest, low-growing celandines to the towering, late-flowering angelicas had long been in residence and were not anxious to leave. Embridge was therefore necessarily a compromise between what we might want and what was already there, between what we, working with spade and mattock in the evenings and at weekends, could do and what the quiet underground forces had been doing and would continue to do all their lives.

But even if we had had the time and the strength we would never have wished to get rid of a million bluebells in order to plant a dozen rose bushes or to uproot an oak tree to replace it with a flowering cherry. Though we might like a small conventional flower garden down at the bottom near the house, we knew it could never rival what was thriving so spectacularly up at the top. Our hyacinths and polyanthuses and pansies might be larger and more colourful but they could never be as numerous as their more humble relatives.

Our predecessors at Embridge had not been enthusiastic gardeners. There was a kitchen garden, walled and rectangular, its dark earth well dug and once no doubt well cultivated but on our arrival growing only thistles. There were a few half-hearted flower beds and some very ancient apple trees. But deep in nettle jungles lurked rusting motor cars; and up at the top was a tangled wilderness which, whatever it might once have been, was now largely brambles and blackthorn.

What, in the past seventeen years, have we achieved? Nothing spectacular. A fence along the road and in front of it some rugosa roses to make a hedge. A little lawn where it is pleasant to sit in the last of the evening sunshine. A path that loops its way up the hillside to a terrace paved with flagstones that came from our dining-room. Flower beds; walls; more paths; more lawns; more beds. Gradually we have been extending our garden upwards towards the top. At the same time the flowers at the top have been tossing their seeds on to our efforts and these have germinated and established little colonies which we have often been most happy to accept. Today the visitor, having passed through the gate and followed the path beneath the huge green umbrella of *Prunus subhirtella autumnalis* (which I planted when it was the merest stripling), having glanced at the tiny goldfish pond and possibly noticed the resident goldfish but failed to see the resident frog, having reached the terrace and looked up at the great apple tree (it was there when we came and I cannot tell you its name), and having continued up the hill beneath an arch now clothed in *Clematis jackmanii*, would stand on another little terrace, this one paved with stones from a nearby beach. Here he would pause for breath and wonder how much further I was going to take him.

Don't worry. If you have come to see our garden, and if by 'garden' you mean what I think you mean, here is where it ends. Here is the unmarked frontier. Beyond is . . . call it what you like, but you must not think of it as wilderness waiting to be tamed or an enemy territory waiting to be conquered; for most emphatically it is neither. But if I take you no further, now that you are here I will just point out one or two things. The first is that you are standing three feet away from a hornets' nest. Does it bother you? I hope not, for they are really quite gentle creatures, and it has been giving us immense pleasure this summer to sit here and watch their comings and goings. At first it was just the queen. She was huge and made a noise like an aeroplane. (In fact on one occasion I thought I heard her approaching and it *was* an aeroplane.) She came every few minutes with materials for her nest, wood pulp that she would turn into brown paper. (You can see a little of it at the entrance to her hole if you come very close.) Then some weeks later the first of her children were born, her workers. Today there is growing activity as workers fly in and out, the nest is enlarged and the young grubs are fed.

Just below the hornets and stretching away to the right you will notice some half dozen cistus bushes. They were at their best a month ago, covered in pale purple flowers. Probably they are not a variety you will recognise, for they are in fact wild. We came upon their parents, a great community of them, while walking through the hills above Perugia. We sat down among them to eat our picnic lunch and afterwards I dug up a few of the smallest seedlings with my picnic knife and we brought them home. They don't seed themselves very readily, but with Lesley's help they managed to produce a few children, and these are they. They are a little elderly now and so perhaps next spring we will be planting out the grandchildren.

The brooms growing in the grass just above them – they too are over now – came from another hillside – in Brittany. I can never feel quite the same affection for a plant that arrives in a black plastic container from a garden centre.

Above the broom the grass is still uncut, cocksfoot and false oat standing waist high among the lower-growing meadow grass and Yorkshire fog. Further up the hillside the bracken grows even higher – well above my head – and at the top are the trees. There is a path to the top, and this I cleared a few weeks ago for the benefit of a visiting friend. It is always my hope that visitors will want me to escort them up this path and then down on the other side by another path. But mostly they don't. They are wearing the wrong shoes or have the wrong sort of legs, or the path looks too rough or too wet or too slippery. And so they just give it a glance and say 'How nice!' At this time of year they will perhaps be thinking how much nicer it would look if the grass were cut. Yes, I agree; and I will be cutting it soon. Just now I am keeping it long for the benefit of the blues. (Why is it that, when I have explained that I am talking about butterflies, people always say, 'Are they the *large* blues?' Of course they are not. Large blues are extinct in England and I most certainly do not have a secret colony here at Embridge. Ours are common blues – and to my eyes the most charming of all our butterflies.) My blues prefer their grass kept long. This is their dormitory. They spend the night clinging to the stems. And in the evening when the sun is behind the hill or again in the morning just after it has risen I go up this path very slowly and count them as I go. They are quite easy to see. One year, without moving, I was able to count twenty and then, moving to another place, a further twenty. But this was followed by a bad year in which our little colony all but disappeared. Since then they have been slowly recovering. Four. Six. Eight. This year, a few days ago, in one little patch of grass I counted eighteen. Elsewhere, though the grass looked just as inviting, there were none. It is the same year after year: always here, on the left of the path. Seldom elsewhere.

Our little slope offers us a whole succession of delights throughout the year. Around the middle of January we start looking out for the first celandine and the first primrose and in February for the first daffodil. By March the entire slope is more yellow than green. By April the violets are appearing, the daffodils are dying, and primroses and celandines are at their best. In May the apple trees come into blossom, and, on the ground, yellow has been succeeded by blue – the blue of our million bluebells. Later this blue is patched with pink as the campions come out. By June the grasses are in flower and in July and August they are joined by the butterflies – meadow browns, gatekeepers and common blues.

I take no credit for any of this. They were all here when we came, though less visible. All I do is to tidy up when they go and then welcome them back the following year. I have done a lot of tidying; and I do not give an equally warm welcome to all who wish to live here. There were, as I have said, too many blackthorns and brambles when we arrived; and there is still rather more hogweed, cocksfoot grass and bracken than I would like. In their place I have planted over 100 trees: oak, ash, beech, hazel, rowan, hawthorn, field maple, Norway maple, four silver birches, two larches and a Scots pine. I have dug paths and made steps and levelled little areas where it is pleasant to sit and I have furnished these with wooden benches. Finally, once a year, armed with scythe or sickle, I clear away the season's growth of grass and bracken and carry it or roll it down the hill to the bonfire.

But gardens are not rooted only in the soil; they are also rooted in the past. And however much we are influenced by the gaily coloured catalogues that come our way and by the latest ideas and suggestions for that ideal garden that could so easily be ours, there will always remain, for most of us, buried deep in our memory, visions of the gardens we knew as children, those flowers we first met and fell in love with when we were scarcely able to walk. I can admire the latest rose or the latest chrysanthemum, triumphs of the plant-breeder's art. But the humble marigold or forget-me-not (so aptly named) or sweet william, if I allow my eyes to settle on it, as a bee or a butterfly will settle, and if I spend a few moments quietly drinking in its beauty, will stir emotions much deeper and stronger. The fuchsias and geraniums in the tiny back garden of the house in London where I was born; the periwinkles that – still clearly visible – grew on some forgotten bank somewhere at Decoy, the cottage near Angmering where we stayed when I was four; orange and yellow azaleas from my grandfather's home on the Hamble; and from Cotchford the phloxes, michelmas daisies, pinks, sweet williams, nasturtiums, marigolds and forget-me-nots: these are the flowers I like to have around me here. And when I feel the need, I go to them. And it may be their colour or it may be their scent, or the way they grow or how they move in the wind or how they look on a particular day against the sky or against the grass – something, some characteristic that is peculiarly theirs, will pull a chord and stir a memory and open a door; and then a sudden most palpable gush of joy will flood through my body.

If it is the flower gardens of my childhood that I see again in our flower garden at Embridge, then it is surely the countryside of my childhood, the Sussex countryside, that I am looking for on the hill above. This is why it has been so difficult to find a satisfying name for it. The obvious name, 'wild garden', is quite wrong. There never was a wild garden in my childhood. No, it is the meadows and woods where I used to wander in search of birds' nests. It is the lanes and footpaths and hedgebanks that I visited on primrosing or blackberrying expeditions. It is the old apple orchard where I went to climb trees. And at the very top it might almost be the top of Ashdown Forest. So part of it is sometimes known as 'the copse' (though I doubt if any of the trees growing there have ever been coppiced in their lives) and part is known as 'the orchard' and the whole is just vaguely 'the top'.

There is something reassuring about a name. It pins a thing down. It identifies it and gives us a feeling that now we understand it. Even a mysterious pain is less worrying once we have attached a name to it. And if we have a choice of names we will prefer the one that seems to suggest and so reinforce the sort of relationship we wish to establish with its owner. It was, I now suspect, the lack of a proper name for the top that left me unsure what precisely I was trying to do up there. Was it in fact a wild garden that I was making? Or a sort of nature reserve? Or a small-scale reincarnation of a pre-war landscape? Or was I merely enjoying myself in my home-made Forest of Arden?

I suppose that whether Arden or garden is your starting point and if you search long enough and range far enough you will sooner or later reach back to that mythical first garden. I describe in *The Windfall* this garden as Eve saw it. And of course in appearance it has much in common with our garden here at Embridge. The big apple tree beneath which she sat: yes, here it is, halfway up the path on the right. It is not quite so big now, for we have had to remove some of its branches to prevent it from falling. The blue butterflies she used to visit on summer evenings: they are the little colony of common blues that live here. The yellow flowers she dug up but had no name for: I could have told her they were primroses. Her feelings for it all were very much as were my feelings for Cotchford when I was a boy. But she did not know – and Adam could only guess – what had been the feelings of God, their father.

It was, after all, his garden, not theirs. He had planted it. The creatures that lived here did so at his invitation. And not until all was ready for them had he brought his two children to it. What had been his hopes? Had they been disappointed? Had it all been a failure? No, I don't think so. Adam had been quite right. They had not been expelled as a punishment for their misbehaviour. Eden was never intended to be their permanent

14

home. It was where they lived, under their father's care, while they were children. It was their nursery garden.

As such it was like all good nurseries. Though the outside world contained, inevitably, both good and evil, safety and danger, pleasure and pain, inside everything was good and safe and pleasant. In the end, however, all children leave home. And so, when they were old enough to look after themselves, they shook themselves free of nursery discipline. They disobeyed. They ate the apple; and thus they learned what now they needed to know – that the world outside was not a wholly good and safe place. They acquired that most necessary piece of wisdom, an ability to distinguish what was good from what was bad.

If this was their last lesson, what was their first? What is any child's first lesson? It is what he learns through playing with his toys. The Garden of Eden was well equipped with toys to play with: indeed it was itself one vast toy. It was a toy world. A toy is a model, conveniently small and conveniently simple, of a reality the child will meet and will need to understand when he is older. As he plays with it – his teddy bear or his building bricks – so he begins this understanding. God, their father, had made the world. Like many another father he wanted his children to inherit from him what he had created and continue the work that he had begun. And he wanted them to do this with all the love and pleasure and pride that had been his. Eden as a nursery was a good and safe place because all nurseries need to be good and safe. As a toy it was good and safe for a different reason. It mirrored the world not as it was but as it might be – that unattainable ideal towards which mankind must strive. Today we look back on Eden as something lost through man's wickedness. It was no more lost to mankind than was my home in Sussex lost to me when at the age of twenty I left it to become a soldier. Lost? I have taken it with me wherever I have gone. It is with me at this very minute more strongly than ever.

The Garden of Eden, then, was not just the first garden for the first man. It was the first nursery and the first toy, setting the pattern for what gardens have been ever since. We play with our toy worlds in our miniature Edens when we are children. We continue playing when we are grown up and have a garden of our own. From the great gardens of the nobility down to the humblest bowl of crocuses in an urban bedsitter, all have this in common: they are worlds which we, god-like, have created and over which we preside, miniature worlds as near to whatever may be our idea of perfection as we can make them. Playing with our gardens – making paths and lawns and rockeries and ponds, or perhaps merely filling a window box with bulb fibre, then planting and sowing and finally tending and enjoying – in all this we are expressing our feelings about the world beyond our garden. We are establishing a relationship between nature and ourselves.

So, if I had failed to find a name for what lay beyond our flower beds, perhaps it was just as well: I should not have been looking for one. 'Copse', 'orchard', 'top', these were all as much a part of our garden as were the more conventional beds and lawns lower down, and whatever I chose to do up there – whether cutting the long grass with my sickle or planting and tending my trees or putting up nesting boxes for blue tits or counting butterflies or watching an interesting beetle or picking a small bunch of the earliest spring flowers for Clare's bedroom or merely lying on my back on the ground and closing my eyes – all this was gardening in its truest sense; and the distinction between catsears and coreopsis, between common vetch and sweet pea, was an artificial one.

I think that subconsciously I had always known this. The garden at Cotchford was, as I have said, my mother's creation. It was she who pored over plant, bulb and seed catalogues, she who gave our gardener his instructions, she who pruned and weeded. My father's share was minimal: to admire and applaud. But just occasionally he would exert his authority, and this was almost invariably in defence of some wild flower that had come uninvited into our garden and which my mother was threatening to remove. I remember in particular the ivy-leaved toadflax that grew across a certain step. No it must not be touched. He loved it. It was his. And 'his' (with a slight smile) that toadflax always remained.

His, too, was the nesting box nailed to the alder by the stream. And it was he, not my mother, who recognised its occupant as a nuthatch. Finally, there was the stream itself. Once my mother had accepted that it was never going to be crystal-clear and asparkle with goldfish she had abandoned it to him; and he and I shared the pleasure of exploring its weedy depths with a fishing net, learning about its strange inhabitants. And surely here was born my present under-standing of the full meaning of the word 'garden'. For the best streams contained more than just what you put in them – goldfish from a goldfish shop – more even than what, as you glanced in, you noticed there. They contained also – and far more excitingly – everything you *might* see there, everything that *was* there.

In the same way, our garden here at Embridge includes not only our cultivated flowers and shrubs and bushes and trees – all the things that we have imported from outside. It includes also all the wild and native plants that were here already, both those we like and those we don't. It includes not only the robins and tits that we invite to our bird table but the willow warbler that sings from the oak tree, the buzzard that circles overhead and the bullfinch that strips the buds off our flowering cherry. It includes not only the red admirals and tortoiseshells that come (as we had hoped they would) to our buddleia but also the vast multitude of other insects, millions upon millions of them, that live here unseen. And best of all it includes those creatures, whether plants or animals, that I shall be meeting for the first time next year – meeting, watching, identifying and learning about. What a lot of pleasure I shall find in their company!

The fact that most of these creatures are free to come and go as they please, that I do not own them or have any sort of control over them, is irrelevant. No gardener can hope to have complete control all the time over his plants, however sternly he tries to discipline them. Control is not essential to the relationship. Not all husbands wish their wives to honour and obey them; and even the sternest ruler must allow his subjects a little freedom to do as they please.

Having widened my definition of the word 'garden', I now want to narrow it a little. A toy is a toy. It is not a tool. It is an end in itself, not a means to an end. Our gardens are toy worlds in which and with which we must feel ourselves free to play as we please. In the real world that exists outside our garden we do many things of which we may be bitterly ashamed. But at least we can make the plea of necessity. We did not wish to destroy our forests but we were cold and needed to warm ourselves. We were hungry and we needed to grow more food. You cannot expect a farmer to put primroses before progress and prosperity. In our imaginary world, our ideal world, there must be no place for excuses such as these.

So, to keep our 'gardens' pure and uncontaminated by outside realities, to enable us to develop within them a philosophy undistorted by outside demands, we must exclude the vegetable garden. Here at Embridge this is easily done: ours is quite separate, surrounded by a wall.

My definition of the word 'garden' would therefore run something like this. It is a place, no matter how small, that is ours and where our fellow humans leave us free to do much as we please. It serves no purpose other than to be what it is, somewhere where we can work out and express that relationship with the natural world that we find most satisfying.

So what is our relationship with the plants and animals in our garden?

If we look to the Bible for our instructions we find them clearly stated in the first chapter of Genesis. 'Be fruitful and multiply and replenish the earth and subdue it: have dominion over the fish of the sea and over the fowls of the air and over every living thing that moveth upon the earth.' Yes, man had first to become the lord and master of the world he had inherited. He had to bring it under his control and teach it to obey him. Once they had left Eden Adam had to become head gardener.

Two pictures come into my mind, both from Normandy.

Normandy is a country of small meadows, apple orchards, trim and sturdy hedges and carefully tended woodlands – of everything that rural England once possessed and is now rapidly losing. Lesley and I like to visit it every year at the beginning of June, in part at least for the pleasure of rediscovering the countryside of our childhood, of walking along lanes where there is little traffic and an abundance of wild flowers. At this time of year the grass is at its greenest and the verges are gay with buttercups, marguerites, clover, foxgloves, orchids, catsears, vetch, speedwell, comfrey and dozens more. On the first occasion I am thinking of we were approaching a village, and here we came upon a woman. She was elegantly dressed. She wore rubber boots and rubber gloves and she held a watering can. She was standing opposite her house, a newly built bungalow within its small square plot of land, and she was contemplating her garden. Two straight rows of cypresses stood sentry along the boundaries on either side, while parallel with the road was a line of cotoneasters. Within these frontiers – apart from a drive almost as wide as it was long – was a grass lawn in which a few circular holes had been dug and planted with conifers. Between the cotoneasters and the road was what was left of the flowery verge that had so delighted us. And now how sad it looked! The grass had vanished and only a few sickly marguerites and buttercups were managing to push their way through the hard dry earth. It was these she was watering, and I knew at once why – and with what. This was now her land. They were trespassers and must go. She was putting them to death.

I think it was the fact that she was doing this with so little effort that most upset me. I could have forgiven her if she had been hacking at them with a mattock. This at least would have been a fair fight. But to sprinkle them with poison without even soiling her fingers seemed the most cold-blooded of murders.

My other picture comes from the public garden at Lisieux. I doubt if there is much to distinguish this from any other public garden in France – except that we happened to be there. It is laid out, as they all are, to an exact and elaborate geometrical pattern like a giant tapestry, and I guess it looks its best when viewed from above in a helicopter. With such a design not only every plant but every leaf must be in place and the seasonal changes that normally occur in a plant's life – growing, flowering and so on – have to be severely controlled. The municipal gardener thus resembles a drill sergeant in charge of a parade of guardsmen, holding them to attention, perfectly spaced, perfectly aligned, all absolutely identical, ready for our inspection.

On this occasion we had reached a platoon of houseleeks (of all plants possibly the least exciting). Where all is so perfect, so boringly uniform, it is of course the one lapse that catches the eye and stays in the memory, the one guardsman who turns to the right when all the others turn left. Here it was sex: in all that sexless garden here was the one sign of life and vigour. One houseleek had disgraced itself. From beneath its skirts there peered a small, illegitimate baby.

These two gardens had one thing in common: both were autocracies. To see them was like watching the lion tamer's performance at a circus. Splendidly dressed, puffing out his chest, he cracks his whip and the poor, dejected king of the beasts snarls, blinks its eyes and jumps wearily through its hoop. The wild animal obeys its master. Houseleeks surrender their ancient freedom. The lords of the forest stand sentry outside their mistress's domain. There is indeed great satisfaction in giving orders and being obeyed; and if it is a satisfaction that eludes us in the outside world, how fortunate if we can find it among the daisies and plantains on our lawn at home.

But though some gardeners remain autocrats like Adam, looking down on their gardens from above, others have become more like Eve. They go there to worship.

Our love of nature is something we inherit from our distant past. The beauty we see in a flower is not something that belongs to that flower – like its petals or its calyx – and which we then happen to notice. It lies in the relationship that exists between flower and man. Our feelings for natural beauty arise out of a past experience – both our own childhood past and our ancestral past – that the natural world has been good to us. It has been our nursery, our home, indeed our mother. 'Mother Nature': the phrase still has real meaning for many of us. Our lives spring from her life, our health from her health. And so we look for that gentle, predictable, reassuring rise and fall of her breathing that tells us she is alive and well, that to-and-fro movement that carries her through the seasons and is repeated year after year. Endless repetition, yet always with a slight difference. Endless variety, yet always within limits of conformity. No two trees – indeed no two leaves – ever exactly alike. No plant – indeed no flower – ever perfectly symmetrical. This is how it has always been. This is how we expect it. This is how we love it. This is beauty.

So those who wish only to command may plant their 100 all-but-identical houseleeks, but those who wish to worship will plant a rose. And the great English landowners of the eighteenth century went even further. They planted hills and valleys, woods and lakes. And they invented the ha-ha wall so that even when their gardens stopped their view continued uninterrupted to the meadows where their sheep and cattle were grazing.

Today most of us must be content with something more modest: a small-scale model of those gardens that were themselves small-scale models of the wider world. Today our meadows have shrunk to lawns, our woodlands to shrubberies, our mountains to rock gardens and our lakes to goldfish ponds. But if our lands are small and our flowers are few they can at least be exotic and they can come to us from all parts of the world. And here we make a sad discovery: they are not always as beautiful as we had hoped.

There are two reasons for this. The first is the obvious one that a plant that grew so happily in the Himalayas or on a sunny sierra may never settle down quite so happily to life in a London suburb. The other reason is that, however well it may feel within itself, it still looks unhappy to us. Like a lion in a circus or a bird in a cage it looks wrong in the setting we have chosen for it. In other words, both plant and gardener need to become acclimatised, to adjust themselves to each other; and in this neither is ever likely to achieve complete success. It is unlikely that the plant will ever be able to look after itself without our help. And in our eyes it will usually only look at home when living either alone in a pot or among fellow foreigners in a specially prepared flower bed. The complete integration of foreigners within a native community – whatever its merits among humans – is seldom pleasing in a garden.

This is something we are very much aware of here at Embridge. At the bottom near the house we have the usual flower beds planted with the usual garden flowers – annuals and perennials – and a few shrubs and bushes. These are mostly cultivated varieties. At the top our plants are mostly wild. The boundary that separates the two is, except in one place, fairly clearly defined and there is very little overlapping. And one of our discoveries is that a garden flower growing among our wild flowers will usually look just as out of place as a wild flower growing in a flower bed. A polyanthus among our primroses is as unhappy as a primrose in a bed of polyanthuses. Fortunately no garden flower is likely to find itself at the top unless I have put it there; and if I don't like it I can easily take it away again. But the reverse is not true and many a wild flower will make its own way uninvited to the bottom – and may be most reluctant to leave. Equally no cultivated flower is likely to interfere seriously with its wild neighbours; but again the reverse is untrue. Hence, although it is possible to worship the primrose or the violet or the bluebell without threatening the existence of any other creature, this is less possible with the polyanthus or the pansy or the hyacinth and still less possible with the more delicate of our garden plants. To worship the rose we must, alas, and however reluctantly, attempt to dominate both its surrounding weeds and its visiting greenfly.

Some time ago I read a gardening article in a Sunday paper. I usually do not read gardening articles, or, if I do, I forget almost at once what they have been telling me. But on this occasion one particular sentence stuck in my memory. 'You will always need some tools to help you fight the unending battle against weeds and pests.' So that was how the writer saw it. And as I read his words I could almost see the gleeful sparkle in his eyes. This was how he *liked* it: he relished the thought of all those battles. He was a born warrior. Did I see it that way too?

I will admit that once I did. Though I had never been the complete autocrat among my plants, though I had on the whole preferred worship to dominion, nevertheless in my early days as a gardener – before we moved to Embridge – I had battled as fiercely as anyone with my weeds and my pests. I well remember the satisfaction it had given me to watch brambles and nettles twisting as if in agony after I had dosed them with some lethal chemical. And even though I was never able to see them – and so had to take their existence on trust – I used to attack with equal determination the red spider mites that I knew to be swarming all over my apple trees.

Then came our move to Embridge. Here our trees were far too big for such treatment. So, feeling a little guilty at my laziness, I left them unsprayed. Did our apple crop suffer? On the contrary, the fruit was both plentiful and clean. Our blue tits had done the work for us. I have since planted many more fruit trees. These, too, I never spray, and they are none the worse for it.

At Embridge, as I have said, we have a kitchen garden, a flower garden, an orchard and a top. Lesley's work is mainly among her vegetables, her soft fruit and her flowers. Mine is among my various trees. If snails eat our seedlings, it is Lesley who does something about it. In my part of the garden, though I may slash and chop and hack and saw, I do not regard this as fighting an enemy but as helping a friend. At times – as, for example, when I am trying to get rid of some nettles – this may seem an equivocation. But it is not; for it is not so much what we do as how we feel when we are doing it that determines whether we are 'for' or 'against'. Undoubtedly it could be said that up at the top I am lucky in that there are so few enemies

23

that need fighting. True — but only because this was how I wanted it. I might equally well have decided to plough it all up and have lawns and rose beds. Then indeed there would have been battles.

I have defined a garden as a place where we express, whether consciously or not, our feelings for the natural world. And I have described how my own gardening philosophy was modified by what I discovered when we came to Embridge. Two further discoveries have confirmed and strengthened it.

The first is the growing realisation of the immense harm that man is doing to the world in which he lives, both in distant tropical forests and close at hand on English farms. Undoubtedly there was once a time when dominating nature seemed the correct thing to do. That was what nature was for: to supply us with our needs like a faithful slave. But even a slave must be healthy and strong if he is to give good service, and it is now increasingly apparent that the natural world is very far from healthy.

My second discovery came from the world of science. It was the change in attitude of the scientist to what he was studying. Classical science — the science that originated with men like Galileo, Newton and Descartes — saw the world as a machine that could be dismantled and examined cog by cog, a machine that was quite separate from the mechanic who was tinkering with it trying to find out how it worked. Such an attitude has served us and is indeed still serving us well. But scientists are today becoming aware of its limitations. There are times when the world is best seen as a living organism that cannot be dismantled for detailed examination and treatment, for it is more than the sum of its separate parts. It is a system of inter-relationships and self-adjustments, a system to which the scientist himself inescapably belongs.

The traditional gardener is like the traditional scientist. He regards himself as separate from his garden. He concerns himself with certain of its components — a bed of roses here, some annuals there and the various other things that he has introduced. And he is concerned too, though in a different sort of way, with the more obvious of the 'enemies' that harm his plants. All the rest, the hundreds of other species that inhabit his garden, he ignores.

I don't know if the modern scientist with his 'systems theory' has ever turned his attention to gardening; but I am sure that if he did he would insist that the word 'garden' be enlarged to include *all* the many forms of life that inhabit it – including the gardener himself. He would certainly warn us that if we did something violent to any one of our many different species we could expect this to have repercussions on all the others – ourselves included. And he would deplore those unending battles that we were apparently so happy to fight.

I like to think he might even suggest that there is now something misguided about what we gardeners are trying to do. If our farmers are busily destroying our native British wild life, they can at least, in their ignorance, plead an excuse. The economics of modern farming and the exhortations that come from the Ministry of Agriculture and from the manufacturers of herbicides, pesticides, fungicides and artificial fertilisers all urge them on their way. But we gardeners are not obliged to imitate them. Indeed there is now every reason for not doing so, for trying to save what little is left, for turning our gardens into sanctuaries for the persecuted refugees of modern agriculture.

I may not have hung a notice on my garden gate saying 'Garden Open Today'. Nevertheless it is open – all day and every day – though not to the passing holiday-maker or member of our local horticultural society, not indeed to humans at all. It is open to all the rest of us, fellow natives, both plant and animal. Here, if I have what they need, I am happy to give them refuge until the day comes when they can return to their homeland, to the fields and the woods that, in a moment of aberration, we once took from them.

Efficiency and the Oil Beetle

WHEN we first came to Embridge there were three things we found living here that were until then quite unknown to us – and which I have yet to find anywhere else.

The first (to give it its more formal name) was lungwort. There was any amount of it sharing a little flower bed at the back of the house with some marigolds.

Lungwort is in fact a wild flower, native to Europe though not to Britain. At some distant time it was introduced into Britain and at some more recent time it was introduced into our garden. But, though a wild flower, it is, like the primrose or the violet or the foxglove, perfectly at home in the flower garden. No one would dream of treating it as a weed. Indeed, so happy does it look, edging the bed that now surrounds our terrace, that I cannot picture it growing in the wild.

Lungwort is its formal name. Even more formal is pulmonaria. But the name we preferred was soldiers-and-sailors. It is also known as soldier-and-his-wife or Josephs-and-Marys or Adam-and-Eve or thunder-and-lightening because the flowers when they first open are pink and later turn blue, giving pink flowers and blue flowers on the same stem. Yet another name is Jerusalem cowslip, which suggests its general appearance. The first buds open early in January on very short stems – far too short to pick. But gradually, as the days lengthen, so too do the stems, until by March they are five or six inches long and hold themselves more elegantly. And the flowering continues into June, thus allowing us six months to enjoy them.

The terrace is a pleasant place for sitting, sunny and sheltered. It is particularly pleasant, therefore, in the early part of the year when the wind is still keen and the soldiers-and-sailors are newly on parade. In February and March on milder days we may prefer to sit elsewhere to enjoy the celandines and primroses and wild daffodils. But a sunny day, whatever the wind, will often find us on the terrace; and to the terrace to visit the soldiers-and-sailors come the first of the bees. In February they come in ones and twos and we greet their return as one of the many eagerly awaited signs of approaching spring. By March and April there is continuous bee-activity among the flowers, and watching it in an idle way gives us added pleasure. A town dweller finds the same sort of pleasure sitting at his window looking down on to the to-ing and fro-ing in the street outside.

To the casual eye bees fall into two categories, 'honey' bees and 'bumbles', the one smooth and small and slender, the other large and round and furry. Both sorts come to the terrace, and as we watched them and got to know them rather better we noticed one of each sort behaving towards the other in a strange way. The 'bumble' was small and black. It moved unhurriedly from flower to flower, the flower heads nodding to mark its progress as its weight pulled them down. The 'honey' bee flew at immense speed. It swooped down on the soldiers-and-sailors, raced two or three times up and down the line of flowers (like a visiting general in a great hurry) and was off. But if during its lightning tour of inspection it came upon a black bumble it would instantly stop and remain hovering in mid air, motionless. Then as the bumble moved unconcernedly among the blossoms the other would stalk it, darting and stopping, all in mid air, keeping out of sight about four inches behind its victim. This would continue while perhaps four or five flowers were visited. Then suddenly came the pounce. The hovering bee would shoot in and grab the unsuspecting bumble and together they would fall to the ground. Bee murder? No, for after a moment both would reappear, the attacker would fly off and the attacked, apparently unhurt, would continue her shopping.

Again and again we watched this happen, day after day throughout the spring and then year after year. What was the explanation? We asked a naturalist friend, a great authority.

But alas his authority extended only to birds, and he could not tell us. This is the trouble with naturalists these days. They know so much about so little. They specialise too narrowly, and outside their chosen field know less than I do. In the end I found the answer quite by chance – in a book I was reading. The two bees, so different in appearance and behaviour, were in fact male and female of the same species. They were 'flower bees' and he was not attacking her. He was making love.

My book mentioned in particular their passion for lungwort. It mentioned also a liking for polyanthus and aubretia, but though we have both, it is only among the soldiers-and-sailors that we have seen them. Nor have we noticed them at any other time of year but the spring when they are courting.

Though we prefer the name we first knew them by, they have another which describes a less visible activity of theirs. They are called 'potter bees', not on account of the way the female wanders from flower to flower but because of the way she makes her nest. She burrows a hole into the ground and furnishes it with several small clay pots. These she fills with a mixture of honey and pollen, then she lays a single egg on top of each and covers it with a lid.

I said that there were three things we found living here that we had never met before. Lungwort and flower bee were two of them. The third was the oil beetle. The link between the first two was obvious, for I never saw a flower bee except on or around the lungwort. The link between bee and beetle is far from obvious. Indeed it is quite invisible to the casual eye, and I must rely on the testimony of that greatest of entomologists, J. H. Fabre.

Oil beetles are not common. They are described as 'local', meaning that they have their small settlements here and there but in between are vast tracts of country where there are none. One of their settlements is in our garden. And I have never found another. Here I meet them frequently on sunny days in the spring, crawling over the grass. They move slowly. They are easy to see and once seen will never be forgotten, for they are like no other creature. Fabre makes no attempt at politeness.

He describes their appearance as 'uncouth', 'clumsy' and 'ugly' and their behaviour as 'disgusting'. But just as one may recoil at first sight from an ugly face but later, as one gets to know its owner better, feel towards him an affection made all the stronger for his very ugliness, so I have developed a special fondness for my oil beetles. The 'disgusting' behaviour that filled Fabre with 'repugnance' has no such effect on me. If you pick up an oil beetle and allow it to explore your finger it will probably in self-defence exude little drops of yellowish liquid from all its joints. It is this oily liquid that gives the beetle its name. It is supposed to be evil-smelling, like the milky liquid you get on your fingers when you pick up a grass snake, and this is intended to discourage would-be assailants. But though Fabre says it makes your fingers 'stink', I have not noticed it; and I have even tried tasting it without ill effects. But I will agree that at first sight there does seem to be something wrong with the beetle's shape. It is as if the Creator had assembled it out of the bits and pieces left over after the other beetles had been made, so that nothing quite matches or is quite the right size. Meeting a female for the first time you think she is carrying something on her back. I am reminded of peasant women in southern Europe weighed down beneath huge bundles of sticks or of the caddis fly larva that crawls around dragging its home-made stick-house with it. But the burden that the oil beetle carries is not fuel for the fire or a home to retreat into. It is itself: its own vast stomach. All other beetles have elegant wing cases, smartly styled, smoothly tailored, gleaming in the sunshine, black, brown, green, red, often irridescent and with spots or stripes. But the oil beetle, so it seems, has to make do with the cast-off and rather bent wing cases originally made for a beetle a quarter its size. And even these are not stitched on properly but overlap in the middle. Finally its antennae have an odd kink as if they had been broken and rather badly glued together.

The life of the young oil beetle begins when its mother lays her eggs in a hole in the ground. It is not often that I can claim to have seen something that Fabre has missed and so I will here proudly state that I have watched an oil beetle laying its eggs.

Fabre was not so lucky, and he had to rely on the British naturalist, Newport. Newport went rather further than I did: he counted them and made the total at the bottom of the hole 4,218. I would certainly agree that there were quite a lot. The eggs are laid in April or May and hatch about a month later. The creature that emerges is so unlike the larva of any other beetle that for a long time it was thought to be a louse. It is long-legged and slender, agile and active, and as the eggs hatch so these tiny yellow creatures race all over the grass. On one occasion they raced all over Fabre. They are searching for flowers and when they find one they clamber up the stem and settle down quietly among the petals waiting for a visitor. When someone arrives (and it may well be a fly or the wrong sort of bee) they scramble aboard and ride away. Most, therefore, are unlucky, going to unsuitable homes. But some find the right host, the flower bee, and are borne off to the bee's hole where the honey pots are waiting. And if one of the riders is even luckier and has come on the right day it will be able to watch an egg being placed on top of the honey. It can then dismount and climb on top of the egg and wait for the bee to put the lid on her pot. Then comes the small creature's first meal. It tears open the skin of the egg and eats the contents. After that it settles down on top of the now flattened egg case that is floating like a raft on the honey and goes to sleep. It wakes up to find it has become a white and very torpid slug-like creature with (fortunately) an appetite for honey. When it has eaten its way to the bottom of the pot – by which time it is about half an inch long – it pupates and emerges in a larval form that is still somewhat slug-like. It pupates again and finally, the following spring, makes its way up into the fresh air a fully developed beetle, hungry now for buttercups.

The obvious lesson to be learned from this is that one species can depend upon another in ways that are not at first sight apparent. Who, coming to Embridge and seeing, as we had, the lungwort that grew close beside the house and the oil beetles that wandered through the grass on the hillside would have imagined any connection between them? Yet I guess that if we dug up all our soldiers-and-sailors we would lose our beetles too.

So when I am assured by a 'spokesman' or an 'authority' or even an 'expert' that no link has been established between something that they are in favour of and something that the rest of us dislike, I am sceptical. Such links may be quite hard to discover. And they are, of course, even harder if one is not a very enthusiastic searcher.

That, as I say, is the obvious moral – that there is much less independence in this world than we commonly like to suppose. But there is another, which occurs to me as I remember the beetle I watched one April afternoon about ten years ago.

I was sitting on a patch of earth that I had recently levelled and was planning to turf when she appeared, making her slow and stumbling way through the surrounding grass to join me. She crawled across the bare earth and, finding a suitable place, stopped and began to dig. She dug awkwardly, as one might expect from such a creature. Her front legs seemed ill adapted for excavating, her back legs ill adapted for pushing the earth out behind her. Frequently the earth she had pushed fell back on top of her. It was as if her legs, too, had come from the oddments box when she was being put together. However, the hole was at last deep enough: her whole body was now inside it. So she backed out and then lowered herself in the other way round. Finally she emerged dragging fragments of earth down into the hole as she pulled herself out.

What impressed me most about this little incident was the beetle's almost unbelievable clumsiness. She and her ancestors had been digging holes like this for maybe millions of years. For millions of years they had been slowly, slowly developing their skill, perfecting their technique and adapting their bodies. And indeed their legs had become the most complicated of mechanisms, reminding me of those multi-purpose pocket knives favoured by Boy Scouts. All beetles' legs are a bit like that. Yet whatever purposes they were designed to fit, digging holes was certainly not one of them; and I felt a longing to devise something better, the front legs ending in a sort of mattock, the back legs shaped more like a shovel. Thus would I reduce the time and effort spent on providing a safe repository for those 4,000 eggs.

But on reflection I see now that I was misguided. Why should I suppose that an oil beetle would welcome my efforts to increase its efficiency? Why should I suppose it was not perfectly happy with things the way they were? What benefits would increased efficiency be likely to bring? Might not such benefits be offset by drawbacks that left the beetle worse off than before? These are the questions I now ask myself; and they ought to be the sort of questions we always ask ourselves before, in our passion for efficiency, we change people's lives, all too often for the worse.

The oil beetle can give a ready answer to our criticism. It may not manage to dig more than three holes in a season but it lays several thousand eggs in each. A weakness in the legs is thus compensated for by magnificent ovaries.

And so it is with other creatures; and so it is with man. Efficiency and inefficiency exist happily side by side and both have a place in our lives. We may wish to change things in order to enjoy greater comfort or greater security or in order to have more time for other desirable things. Greater efficiency may well help us towards these ends. But it should never be thought an end in itself.

Thus when I am given the task of clearing the supper things from the dining table to the kitchen I will use my hands for the purpose, carrying it may be a plate in one hand and two forks in the other. Lesley points out that if instead I used a tray I would be able to carry more things at once and so need to make fewer journeys. Maybe. But why should she assume that I wish to make fewer journeys? I enjoy walking to and fro between rooms, picking up something and putting it down. I find it physically satisfying and a simple enough task to allow my thoughts to wander elsewhere. Whereas piling things up on a tray and fearing all the time that a cup or a glass will topple over the edge requires all my care and attention.

Looking at the larger world beyond Embridge I am becoming

more and more convinced that the blind pursuit of efficiency is doing us immense harm. It has led us to specialisation, which may well have been good, but it is now leading on to over-specialisation, which is dangerous. It may well have been a good thing when the carpenter specialised and became a chairmaker, but it became less good when the chairmaker specialised and became the man who operates the machine that cuts the dowels that pin the rails to the legs.

The supreme example of pointless over-specialisation is that we now have in our world two vast groups of men who, independently of each other, are engaged in making the most highly efficient engines of destruction whose one and only purpose is that they should never be used. If only they could look up from their work for a moment and then look around at other parts of the world and then perhaps meet and talk things over, they would surely agree what a ludicrous waste of time it all is.

Only marginally less alarming is the over-specialisation and super efficiency to be seen in our attempts to grow more food. From the Minister of Agriculture and the President of the National Union of Farmers down to the humblest packer of battery eggs, everyone is pursuing his task on the narrowest possible front. Looking neither to left nor right, all forge blindly ahead. More tonnes of wheat per hectare, more sacks of fertiliser sold, more ingenious pesticides invented, more money in the bank. Success after success after success. Yet when it is all added up and all the battery chickens that have managed to stay alive have come home to roost I don't doubt that the total will be reckoned a failure.

Our world is full of holes and hole-makers. Some of the holes are brilliant feats of engineering. Others are not. It doesn't follow that the best holes are drilled for the best purposes. It is the purpose that matters. I would rather have oil beetles in my garden drilling holes for their eggs than humans drilling holes for their oil.

The Egg, the Fox and the Dagger

I HAVE been pondering on the various pleasures I enjoy as an amateur naturalist and I have decided that they are of three different kinds, and that each kind represents a step towards a closer relationship with the natural world.

The first pleasure and the first step is that of recognition, of being able to attach a name to what I have found. It may be something I have seen often enough but whose name I have only just learned; or it may be something new that I have happened on for the first time. But more often it will be just the simple pleasure of recognising an acquaintance: like the pleasure of being able to say 'Good morning, Mrs Brown. Good morning, Mr Smith' as we jostle with our fellow citizens on market day.

I first became an amateur naturalist rather than a mere nature lover when, at the age of thirteen, my father gave me a copy of Kirkman and Jourdain's *British Birds*. As a young ornithologist, keen to add to the growing list of birds I could identify, I used to spend as much time as possible out in the country with my binoculars, examining whatever I heard or saw. Then, on my return, I would thumb through Kirkman until I had matched it up. And it was not long before I could name by its song or its appearance almost any bird that came my way in the course of an afternoon's ramble.

Today, though I would still hope to be able to identify any bird I met, I no longer go searching for them. If I am searching for anything, it is now more likely to be a flower or an insect. And Fitter and Blamey's *Wild Flowers of Britain and Northern Europe* and *The Oxford Book of Insects* have become as well thumbed as my still surviving *British Birds*.

But names, alas, are harder to remember than once they were

and I may have to remind myself more often than I would wish of the precise differences between the various hawkweeds, hawkbits and hawkbeards.

This, the first of my three pleasures, has the particular merit that it can be enjoyed whenever I wish. At any time of the year Lesley and I can go for a walk and entertain ourselves by counting – and naming – the number of different wild flowers that we see in bloom. On our holiday last summer we named over 100. There is also the annual pleasure of welcoming back the first arrivals: the first celandine, the first chiff-chaff, the first scarlet tiger moth. Even if we never see anything new or unusual there is still much pleasure in greeting old friends.

Once a bird or a flower or an insect has been tracked down, the book will tell you something about its behaviour; and naturally one of the things I wanted to know about my birds was when and where they built their nests. I never became an egg collector, but I most certainly became a nest seeker, and I would hunt up and down hedgerows and peer into bramble patches and work my way through reed beds, searching, searching. At Cotchford I had until the beginning of May; so mostly it was blackbirds, thrushes, hedge sparrows and wrens and, if I was lucky, a long-tailed tit. At Stowe I had the rest of the season and I have memories of whitethroats and reed warblers and on one occasion a redstart. And it was then that I discovered the second of my three pleasures.

This is the pleasure of being a spectator. One can see a bird sitting in a bush or flying overhead: this, unless it is something rare, is not particularly exciting. Much more exciting is to watch it visit its nest to feed its young. One can of course remain an ornithologist, watching and recording with scientific accuracy the number of caterpillars consumed per hour. This may well be pleasure enough for some; but not for me. The pleasure I am thinking of is the one we share with the audience at a theatre: of watching from the shadows, of seeing without being seen, of eavesdropping on someone's private conversation, of taking a surreptitious glance into someone's private life.

Where I live, if you want to enjoy a few minutes of domestic bird-life, a good vantage point is the top of a cliff. Here, sitting on the short grass, you are in the upper circle and the stage is below you; and at the right time of year you will almost certainly be able to watch the comings and goings of at least one pair of herring gulls together with the anxious waitings, eager welcomings and joyous feastings of their children.

I have used these three adjectives deliberately and I realise that this is something the serious ornithologist would deplore. Birds do not have human emotions. Anthropomorphism is forbidden. But I do not look at birds through ornithological eyes only. I am like the playgoer who, though he knows that the actors are only actors, likes to imagine them as the characters whose parts they are playing. Indeed the acting can sometimes be so good that it is hard to know where truth ends and imagination begins; and this is as true of bird as it is of man.

I remember in particular a little drama that Lesley and I watched one afternoon many years ago from a cliff top near Start Point. There were three actors on the stage below us: Father Herring Gull, Mother Herring Gull and Egg. When the curtain went up Mother and Egg were on the stage. Enter Father swooping in from the sea. It was now his turn to baby-sit while Mother stretched her wings and found something to eat. Brief duologue in which Mother gives Father his instructions and Father says, 'Yes, yes, yes. Of course, dear. Of course'. Exit Mother. Father settles himself on top of Egg and fidgets his wings into position. There. Now he can relax. No. He is not quite comfortable and fidgets again . . . and then again. Unfortunately the more he fidgets, the more uncomfortable Egg becomes. Every time he moves Egg moves too. Gradually it dawns on him (and we could see it dawning) that Egg is moving nearer and nearer to the edge of the precipice. He is now desperately trying to push it back, but alas he is only making matters worse. How easy it is for the onlooker to see what ought to be done. 'Get your wing the *other* side of it.' In vain. Egg is now on the verge. Nothing can save it. Over it goes, a sheer drop of some twenty feet. Smash!

And there is poor Father peering over to see what has become of it. He is still peering when Mother returns. 'What are you doing? . . . *What has happened to our Egg?*'

Kirkman desribes what he calls the 'wild cacchination' of the herring gull thus: Head raised: 'eow! eow! eow!'. Head lowered: 'ee-er, ee-er, ee-er'. But on this occasion we had no need of Kirkman. We knew perfectly well what she with her head raised and he with his head lowered were saying to each other.

Thus my second pleasure brings the actors alive, turns them from a list of *dramatis personae* into individual characters. Yet though they perform, I merely watch. And so my third pleasure – and the final one in our relationship – is to find myself, not a spectator sitting unnoticed in the upper circle, but a fellow actor on the stage. If it was a privilege to be allowed to watch, it is an even greater privilege to be offered a part.

One becomes, I know, a fellow actor when at a picnic the wasp arrives and gets mixed up with the jam, or when, later in the evening, the mosquito settles on one's arm. But I am not thinking of those occasions when man plays his customary role – that of enemy to be avoided or supper to be eaten. I am thinking of those very much rarer occasions when, to our surprise, we are given (or appear to be given) a much more unusual and altogether more flattering part.

Yes, indeed, on such occasions we are flattered; and we feel greatly honoured when an animal forgets to be either afraid or fierce and comes to us for our help. Androcles, even if he had never seen his lion again after their first meeting, would still have had a story worth boasting about.

I can think of two occasions when I have been invited to become a sort of Androcles to a creature in need. On both occasions, although this was how I saw myself, I will admit that the creature I helped may have seen me rather differently. But that is no matter.

On the first occasion it was after dark on a June evening and I was in the kitchen doing the washing up when there came an unexpected and very violent battering on the window. I opened it and a large moth flew in, made for the light and flew round it in the usual frantic moth-like manner. I reached up my hands and caught it quite easily. I held it until its flutterings had stopped and then very cautiously opened my hands to see what it was. The moth remained clinging to my finger, gently quivering. I will admit that I did not immediately recognise it. Not until later, with the help of my *Oxford Book of Insects*, did I discover it to be a female fox moth.

The fox moth likes moorland country. The female lays her eggs on the stems of heather, and in order that these eggs should be less visible to the passer-by, she makes them look exactly like tiny white heather bells. I know this not only because my book told me so but because when my moth eventually flew away into the night I found that she had deposited on my finger in a neat line, stuck down with her own patent glue, four heather-bell eggs.

Why had she done that? No doubt an entomologist could give me the scientific reason. But I preferred to imagine that she had come from Dartmoor, had been blown south by a spell of bad weather, and had lost her way. She had searched for heather and found only grass. She had searched until she could wait no longer. Her time had come and so, seeing me, she had knocked on my window to seek my help.

I did not fail her. I was conscious of her trust and of my responsibility. I looked after her children until they were two inches long, striped black and yellow like football stockings and well able to fend for themselves. My duties as foster parent discharged, maybe I ought to have driven them back to the moor. But my insect book assured me that they would thrive equally well on a diet of brambles. I found them a bramble bush and wished them well.

On the second occasion I played the part not of foster parent but of house agent.

It was the end of August and Clare and I were sitting on the lawn having breakfast.

'There's a caterpillar on your shoulder,' she said; and so there was.

It was about an inch and a half long and gaily coloured, and I didn't recognise it. I took it off and put it on the grass nearby and at once it began to hurry towards me. I moved out of its way, and still it came towards me. I moved behind it and it turned round, raced up to me and began to climb my trousers. I put it on a leaf and put the leaf on the flower bed. The caterpillar dropped to the ground, hurried back and again climbed my trousers. So I left it there, settled in a fold by my pocket, while we ate our eggs. But after that I needed to go indoors for some coffee. So I put my caterpillar on the jersey I had just taken off, hoping it would be content with that while I was away. When I came back Clare told me it had left my jersey and was now somewhere under her chair. I looked but failed to find it; and we began drinking our coffee.

Then I saw the caterpillar. It had seen me and was hurrying back. It climbed quickly over the bits of breakfast that were in its way, raced up my trousers and settled once again in a fold by my pocket.

What did it want and how could I help it? The first thing was to find out just who it was. So together we went indoors to consult my book. Luckily it was sufficiently gaudy for there to be no doubt. It was the caterpillar of the grey dagger moth and my book told me that when they were ready to pupate they searched for the fallen and decayed branch of a tree and either squeezed behind a piece of loose bark or else made themselves a hole in the rotting wood. That explained it! My trousers were oldish and to my caterpillar they either looked like loose bark or smelled like rotting wood. Possibly both. Nevertheless I was not prepared to hand them over to be used as a bedroom for the next six months.

For occasions such as this I have a glass case which I can furnish within to suit most needs. I put the caterpillar inside and went off to look for some genuine rotting wood. After hunting for a while I came back with a short length of dead apple branch. It had plenty of loose bark but the wood was rather hard. So I took it into my workshop and drilled a hole half an inch across and rather more than an inch deep. Then I offered it to my caterpillar.

It was delighted and at once began to explore the house I had made for it. It climbed the bark. It peered into possible cracks. Finally it reached the top, saw my hole and got inside. After a moment it came out and I feared it was dissatisfied. But no, the hole was ideal. All it lacked was a front door. For the next few minutes the caterpillar, keeping its back legs inside the hole, explored round the edge with its front legs, gathering in its jaws fragments of wood and leaf and carrying them back inside.

I left it and brought in the breakfast things, and when I next went to look I saw that half the opening was already covered over. Soon there was not enough space left to squeeze through and so the last of the work was done from the inside.

I left the caterpillar to sleep in peace – and hurried upstairs to record exactly what had happened.

Those, then, are my three steps towards a closer – and I believe a proper – relationship with the non-human world. And of course the naturalist, the biologist, will have stopped short after the first. He is quite right to do so, but he must not think that he can tell us all we need to know about nature any more than the doctor can tell us all we need to know about humanity.

In my first step I saw the natural world through the eyes of the scientist. A plant or an animal was what my reference book said it was. I could look it up and beneath its picture read a brief description of its appearance and its habits. It is at this stage that flowers are picked and pressed, birds' eggs are blown, butterflies and moths are pinned on to a board and animals are stuffed and put into cases in museums. Or rather this is what used to be done when I was a boy. Today this is considered cruel and we prefer other methods of collecting and recording, such as taking photographs. But whatever method we choose, this first step is an essential one. We must start by learning what the scientist has to teach us. If I had been unable to identify my fox moth and my grey dagger I should never have enjoyed so much pleasure in their company.

In the second stage of the relationship creatures are no longer merely representatives of their species. They come alive. They move. They are individuals in their own right, going about their everyday affairs in their own private worlds. They are fish in a fishpond, caterpillars in a shoe box, ants in a formicarium, animals in a zoo and flowers in a vase of water. We can watch them; but we ourselves remain outside, spectators, peering through the glass or between the bars. Their world is not our world.

In the third and final stage the bars are pulled down. Our two worlds become one. This is the relationship we normally establish with only a few carefully selected species: our garden flowers, perhaps, and almost certainly the household cat.

As yet we are a long way from regarding every beetle as a first-class citizen or granting equal rights to every dandelion. We have, after all, only very recently reached this stage in our relationship with our fellow humans, particularly if they belong to a different race.

Very many years ago, when I was about six years old, I was walking through a wood with my parents. The track was a wide one, practically a lane, and across it, in front of us, wriggled a snake. I can still see it, and I know without any doubt that it was an adder. I bent down to stroke it and my father, with a fierce jerk on my arm, pulled me away.

'Why did you do that?' I cried.

'It would have bitten you.'

'But I was only going to stroke it. I was not going to hurt it.'

'I don't think the snake could have been sure about this.'

I thought for a moment. 'If I had offered it some food first,' I said, 'would it then have been sure?'

'I don't think so. You see, if you had offered it some bread, it would have said to itself: "Here is some bread. Let me eat it." And when you offered it your hand, it would have said: "Here is a hand. Let me bite it."'

Yes, I had much to learn. And I had to start at the beginning. But though the adult has much to teach the child, the child in return has something to teach the adult. For our journey is, or should be, a circular one in which we end up where we began, returning to the world we left when first we went to school, and bringing with us the wisdom and knowledge we have gathered on our way.

The child's world is a single indivisible world in which all creatures, human and animal, live together as equals. Instinctively he feels this to be the truth – as indeed it is.

But in order to understand it, in order to learn how it works, we need to examine it bit by bit; and so we take it to pieces, separating it into its various layers – its species and subspecies, its races and classes. At school I learned how to distinguish a verb from a noun, a Cavalier from a Roundhead, a logarithm from an antilogarithm and an atom from a molecule. When we have finished studying the world in this way and have learned all we can about it, perhaps we remember it as we once knew it. But can we ever put it together again?

This is the question that today faces not only the middle-aged adult but humanity as a whole. Can we, the human race, reassemble a world that, over the millennia, we have been taking apart? Can we put it together before it totally disintegrates?

There is not much time left. The child is waiting for us, beckoning to us. We must hurry.

Beetles to Betelgeuse

WHEN, in the second chapter of Genesis, the Lord God brought every beast of the field and every fowl of the air to Adam to see what he would call them, he was taking that most necessary first step in bringing man and nature into closer relationship with each other.

Whether Adam would be making a scientific study of the natural world or merely enjoying his surroundings, he had first to give names to its individual components. Today most of the world's separate parts are already named: all we need to do is learn them. The naturalist has to learn them all — or rather all those that lie within his particular field of study. The nature lover may think he can get away without learning any: that he can walk through the countryside and look at the flowers and listen to the birds and enjoy it all without bothering about names. But he will miss a lot.

Just as we enjoy the company of our fellow humans the more because we can distinguish Miss Smith from Miss Brown without fear of muddling them up, so it is with chaffinches and robins, with celandines and buttercups. But equally, just as we have no special wish to increase our circle of acquaintances indefinitely, tapping every stranger on the shoulder and asking his name, so it is in the non-human world. With both, we need our friends. We welcome their companionship — some more than others. But there comes a point when we are satisfied.

There are, admittedly, those enthusiasts who collect for collecting's sake. There are bird lovers who will accompany ornithologists to distant marshes in the hope of a glimpse of a bearded tit, which they will then proudly add to their list. But most of us prefer to stay at home watching whatever comes to our bird table or nests in our nesting box or sings to us from the

43

top of our apple tree. Nuthatch, blue tit, blackbird: thank you for coming.

I started with birds. I became an amateur ornithologist at the age of thirteen. Naming them meant recognising them not only from their appearance but also from their song. It also meant identifying the various nests I found. Here was enough to keep me busy for many years. I didn't have time for flowers. In any case, flowers, in the opinion of most boys, were for girls. And so it wasn't until I married Lesley that a wild flower book was added to my elderly bird book.

Flowers, too, need naming if you are to enjoy their company to the full. Unnamed, they too often remain unseen. The eye passes over them as it does over the faces of strangers in a crowd. It is only when they catch and hold your attention – ah, there's a familiar face! – that they have any hope of impressing you with their beauty.

Today, helped by the occasional reminder at the beginning of the season of the difference between bugle and betony or between the various hawksbeards, hawkbits and hawkweeds, Lesley and I can usually recognise most of the flowers that live around here. And I don't think that the addition of something small, white and inconspicuous, however rare, would add much to our pleasure.

So, after I had named my flowers, I turned my attention to insects.

Insects, as it happened, had been my first love. At the age of four I had developed a fondness for butterflies, and by the age of eight I was keeping beetles in matchboxes. There may not be much to learn about flower behaviour, but there is an immense amount that even entomologists are still busy learning about the behaviour of insects. Recognition is only the first step into a world in which every new creature we meet seems to have its own uniquely improbable way of conducting its affairs.

It is when you begin identifying insects (insect book on lap) that you become aware of the dividing line between nature lover and naturalist. Every bird, from the common robin to the less common bittern, has its English as well as its Latin name. So does every flower. Indeed some of our commonest have more than one. The daisy, for example, has a whole string of other names, such as baby's pet, baiyan-flower, banwood, bennergowan, bessy-bairnwort, billy button, cat posy, curl-doddy, ewe-gowan, golland, innocent, little open star, Mary Gowlan, silver pennies and white frills, showing that our most beloved of wild flowers had been taken into our hearts long before dictionaries had been invented. Our butterflies, too, have English names, and so, despite the fact that there are around 2,000 of them, do our moths – though I would be surprised if anyone who was not a lepidopterist could distinguish a July highflyer from a grey pine carpet or a treble-bar. But we are not on such familiar terms with our beetles. A near relative of the devil's coach horse is known only as *Creophilus maxillosus*. Skimming through an insect book, you can see at a glance which creatures have managed to draw attention to themselves and which have not. Only an entomologist, I guess, is aware of *Xanthogramma pedissequum*. Even a naturalist, for all his other qualifications, would probably confess ignorance.

This, of course, is the trouble: the more expert they become, the narrower is their field of research. We, having found and identified (with their help) our oak tree, are content to admire it. But they, to understand it, disappear beneath the ground to examine its roots. The roots divide and subdivide and each branch claims its specialist. They have been underground so long and have probed so deeply that anything they say is heard only by those nearest to them. Have they nothing to say to us? Yes. There is one thing they have discovered that we can all understand: indeed we had guessed it all along. The tree we are looking at is a single living tree. The world and all its inhabitants is a single living world.

It is like that small boy who, having played with his clockwork toy for a while, then took it to pieces to find out how it worked. 'Why have you done that?' asked an astonished mother. 'So that I can put it together again,' was his answer.

If this is what the scientist is doing, it is also what we all do.

Naming is the first step in taking to pieces so that we can put together again. The naturalist names in order to study. We who are not naturalists name the better to enjoy. And since I could not enjoy what I could not see, there was no particular point in being able to name what I was unlikely to meet. I was good enough on the various birds, flowers, trees, mammals, insects and amphibians that were sufficiently common round here to make their presence felt. Fungi were Lesley's affair: it was she who needed to know whether or not they were edible. I added a few grasses. I thought I might try spiders but I found the spider book that Lesley gave me one Christmas daunting rather than encouraging.

This left me with one category which, though not coming within the field of the naturalist, was certainly visible and varied enough. The stars.

My fondness for darkness began – in a negative way – when I stopped being frightened of it. I remember the occasion quite well. We were at Cotchford. Would I go up to the attic to fetch something? There were no lights. I had no torch, no candle. But I went, feeling enormously brave; and I returned, to the praise of my family, feeling enormously proud of myself. The next step, many years later, was when I walked back from Ashdown Forest through Posingford Wood one night: in spite of the darkness I had found my way. So when, six years ago, I was asked to list my pleasures, these included 'wandering over hills and under trees, especially at night'.

I suppose the first and most obvious reason for preferring to do my wandering at night rather than during the day is that I can do it where and how I please: there is no one to watch. Hilltops are exposed places, visible for miles around, and I'm not quite sure what local farmers might think if they saw me up there among their sheep. But that too is a negative reason for liking darkness. A more positive reason is that at that late hour, when most people are in bed, I am unlikely to come upon others doing the same thing. I have the world to myself. And then there is the complete contrast between day and night. During the day it is the detail that catches the eye, the small things that hold the attention. You hear a thrush – or possibly an approaching car. You notice a patch of violets – or possibly an empty beer can. And so on. But at night there is little to see and less to hear. The small things – both pleasant and unpleasant – have vanished away, and you become conscious instead of the larger things – shapes and distances.

Nights vary enormously. The most universally admired, that of a full moon in a cloudless sky, is, to the night wanderer, perhaps the dullest. The moon dominates the sky. The stars are invisible. One's surroundings are scarcely invisible enough. When the moon is up I prefer a sky patterned with high cloud. For then you get movement. The moon travels through the clouds. You can sit on the ground and watch its progress, as it comes and goes, brightening the cloud's edge a moment before emerging, then sailing free into the jet black sky. The clouds, which in the day time you can watch moving across the sky, at night remain stationary. It is the moon that moves. Other nights, too, have their charm: misty nights, murky nights, windy nights. And then there are the nights with neither cloud nor moon, when the sky is bright with stars.

Some little while ago, happening on a pile of old books in our attic, I noticed *The Times Guide to the Night Sky* for 1975. So that was when I made my first attempt. The guide was in remarkably good condition, showing how quickly the attempt had been abandoned. Last year, with greater determination, I tried again. I knew, as we all do, the three major constellations and I could identify the Pole Star lying midway between two of them. But beyond that all was anonymous.

The first thing that surprised me was that of all the stars only two possessed ordinary, homely English names: the Pole Star and the Dog Star. All the rest we had left to the astronomer; and what an astonishingly heterogeneous collection of unpronounceable names he had chosen. Some, like Arcturus, were Latin. Others, like Betelgeuse, seemed French. But most, like Deneb and Dubhe, Algenib and Caph, were Arabic. Instead of naming the individuals, we, the ordinary star-gazers on our hilltops, had preferred – so it seemed – to group our stars into

47

constellations. But though these had names that were familiar enough, I found most of them extremely hard to identify. They trailed aimlessly across the sky and included stars far too dim for me to see at all.

So individuals it would have to be. It was not easy. Even a few clouds would upset the pattern. But with every success – a new star identified or an old one recognised without help – I became more enthusiastic. And gradually I discovered, as my collection grew, how much more they were than mere names that needed a dictionary to give me their pronounciation. A relationship was developing between us which, surprising though it may seem to most people, is, I guess, familiar enough to the mariner. The stars were becoming my companions. As with insects and with humans, of all the millions in existence, I needed to be able to attach names to only the tiniest handful. A bare fifteen, it was.

The *Times Guide* now lives permanently in the left-hand pocket of my anorak and a small dim torch lives in the right. I have a choice of four hills. Which shall it be tonight? I climb quickly against the cold winter wind, eyes on the ground ahead of me to avoid stumbling. Not until I have reached the top and turned to face the south where the stars are brightest do I look upwards. I start with Orion, surely the most recognisable of all constellations. Beneath and to the left is Sirius, the Dog Star, and the brightest of them all. From here my eye swings outwards and upwards: Procyon, Castor and Pollux (that very recognisable pair) and thence to Capella, my favourite of them all because she never sets. There are others. Vega and Deneb, two members of the great triumvirate, are now low in the sky; Altair, the third, has vanished. The Square of Pegasus points the way to Algol, and from there you can return to Orion by way of Aldebaran and – the merest hint of whiteness – the Pleiades. I stare upwards for a while, greeting them all, and feeling much as a man might do when he enters a room that is warm and welcoming with familiar faces.

It is well past midnight: time for home. And so I begin to walk, very slowly, eyes upwards, down the hill. This is the moment of putting together. What comes of it? Sometimes nothing. The stars take their places, sinking back into anonymity; and I continue down the hill to where I can see a terrestrial light waiting to welcome me. But sometimes there is something more. I won't attempt to describe it. I will only say that I can now understand why in the past – and before astronomers had corrected him – man had looked upwards to find his God.

From beetles to Betelgeuse: I now have names enough. Botanist, biologist and astronomer: they have all lent a hand and helped me on my way. But in the end each of us must make his own solitary pilgrimage towards whatever lies at the centre of it all.

The Windfall

A Story

With engravings by Kenneth Lindley

*So God created man in his own image,
in the image of God created he him;
male and female created he them.*

*And God blessed them, and God said
unto them, 'Be fruitful, and multiply,
and replenish the earth, and subdue
it: and have dominion over the fish
of the sea, and over the fowl of
the air, and over every living thing
that moveth upon the earth.'*

Foreword

SOME THREE thousand years ago, the Israelites, after years of
captivity in Egypt and further years spent wandering across the
desert, had at last reached the Promised Land and could settle
down to become a nation. 'Where did we come from?' 'How
did it all start?' Now for the first time it could be recorded.
Memories stretched back a little way. Memories of memories
stretched a little further. And behind them lay those stories
that had been passed from generation to generation: the
myths. 'In the beginning . . .' Whether or not it was literally
true, here was the nearest they could get to their starting point,
that historic root they needed to anchor themselves to the
world.

Those myths still survive. They are not the starting point of
our history, for we are a different race and have a greater
knowledge of our past. They are instead the starting point of a
religion. Consequently, if we look to them for a truth, it will be
a religious or moral truth that we hope to find. Thus the story
of Adam and Eve tells us something about the relationship
between God and man, of sin and punishment.

But is this the only possible interpretation?

If you are writing about gardens, thinking about gardens, then
at some point your thoughts are bound to turn to that famous
first garden with its famous first gardener. What could I learn
from them? This led me to wonder if, men being what they are,
Adam had perhaps been awarded an honour not altogether
deserved. In our garden here at Embridge, it is really Lesley
who is gardener-in-chief. It is she who digs and manures and
sows and plants and tends and harvests. I do other things,
mainly up at the top among my trees where it is wilder. Her

tools are spade and trowel. Mine are sickle and saw. Was it perhaps more like this in Eden?

That was how *The Windfall* began, and it led me to the discovery that those early myths held within them another truth and could be interpreted in an altogether different way. So what set off as an attempt to restore to Eve the credit that had been denied her, ended up as a retelling of the first seven chapters of Genesis in order to show – with as little alteration to the main events as possible, but with quite a lot of additional clothing – how closely they paralleled the past 50,000 years of mankind's history.

In an allegory that uses familiar figures in a familiar setting, there is a danger that something of the familiar interpretation will linger to cloud the new. Surely God is still God and Adam still represents mankind? Surely sin and punishment still come into the argument? No. None of these things. And so, to help the reader start off in the right direction and with the right expectations, I would like to preface my story with an introduction to the two main characters and say a little about the two main events.

First, Adam and Eve. In the original myth they had been individuals, quite literally the first man and the first woman. In the biblical interpretation they sometimes represent their two sexes and sometimes Adam will represent both sexes at once – mankind in general. In my story they represent two different ways of looking at the world.

Adam sees it as something that exists outside himself. He distinguishes between what is 'him' and what is 'not him', and so between what is his and what is not his, between friend and foe, good and bad. And naturally it is his ambition to understand and tame as much of this outside world as possible – both its human and its non-human elements – and get them to work for his benefit.

Eve, on the contrary, sees herself as part of the world, rather as our hand is part of our body. The world – the whole world – is her home, and all its many and various inhabitants share it with her.

Most men have in them more of Adam than of Eve; most women are more Eve than Adam. But this need not be so, and we can move from the one to the other in the course of our lives. And maybe mankind too can change in the course of the centuries. Scientists, for example, in the days of Newton and Descartes, saw the world as Adam saw it; but many of them – biologists and theoretical physicists in particular – are today seeing it through the eyes of Eve. Buddhists have always seen it that way.

Up to now Adam has been the dominant partner and he has undoubtedly led us to great triumphs. But he is now heading for disaster. Ours is a living world and a finite one. It is not immortal, nor is it necessarily able to do all we demand of it. Our battles against nature and among ourselves now threaten the existence of us all.

We talk of 'the march of civilisations' and we have a picture of a great army of humanity moving forward out of the morass of prehistory towards some distant mountain top. I think that a better picture would be of a sailing ship moving forward against the wind. For the last 50,000 years or so she has been on the port tack, Adam has been at the helm and she has made excellent progress. But now there are rocks ahead. It is time to go about. It won't be easy but it might just be possible. I believe that if human civilisation is to continue for another 50,000 years, Eve – and I mean, of course, that attitude towards our surroundings that she represents – must have her turn at the wheel.

And now for my two main events. The first is the expulsion from the garden. In my story this is not a punishment for a sin. It is to be interpreted as that event that occurred in the life of mankind when, between the Mesolithic and the Neolithic Ages, we stopped being hunters to become farmers. As hunters we had been like the rest of creation, both plant and animal: we had taken the world as we had found it, helping ourselves to what we had wanted and ignoring the rest. As farmers we set out to make it the way we wanted it to be. Eden had been God's world. Outside, it was to become Adam's.

The other event is the Flood. I have moved it from the distant past to the not-so-distant future. I doubt if we can avoid it. Indeed it seems at times as if we scarcely wish to avoid it. And it may well be necessary to set us on our new course. I just hope we survive it. But who can tell? And so my story ends, quite literally, in mid-stream.

I

Then the Lord God planted a garden in Eden away to the east, and there he put the man whom he had formed.

The Lord God made trees spring from the ground, all trees pleasant to look at and good for food; and in the middle of the garden he set the tree of life and the tree of the knowledge of good and evil.

He told the man, 'You may eat from every tree in the garden, but not from the tree of the knowledge of good and evil.'

Then the Lord God said, 'It is not good for man to be alone. I will provide a partner for him.' And he made him a wife.

Eve went into her garden. She had spent the day working. She had been along the edge of the forest to gather food. She had penetrated a little way under the trees to collect fallen sticks for her fire. She had returned home to prepare meat for their evening meal. She had fastened a new handle to an axe and resharpened the tip of one of Adam's spears. Then she had gone to the place where the nut trees grew and gathered some of the long, thin, straight wands that came up each year and these she had begun to weave into baskets. And now, having worked hard, she was going to enjoy the last few rays of the evening sunshine. It was autumn. The long stems of the grasses were turning brown and the berries on her trees were red.

Eve loved her garden. She had made it herself. That is to say she had made it without Adam's help. The flowers and bushes and trees that grew there had mostly put themselves there. And the birds and butterflies and other insects that came there came because they wanted to. She couldn't take credit for that. But there was quite a lot she had done, more perhaps than Adam suspected. She had trimmed the bushes when they became too big. She had made paths leading to the various places where she liked to sit. She had hollowed out these places so that they were smooth to lie in and sheltered from the wind. And then there were her flowers.

Some, like the grasses and bushes, had always been growing there; but there were others that she had first encountered on her expeditions to the forest in search of food. She had picked little bunches and brought them back and pushed them into the soft, moist earth. For a day or two they had stayed fresh and given her pleasure; then they had faded. They had never lasted as long as those that grew there naturally.

One day, however, stooping to pick a flower, she had accidentally pulled it up by the root; and when she had planted *this* in the earth (not knowing at all what to expect) she had been delighted to find that it not only survived for much longer but that new blossoms came. So it seemed that if she scooped deeply enough and pulled very carefully, it was possible to gather the entire plant; and this could be moved to another place where it would then continue to grow.

This was a great discovery and from then on, whenever she went walking, she would carry with her a special stick, and if she came upon a new flower she would ease it out of the ground and bring it home. Sometimes she was successful; sometimes not. Sometimes the roots went too deep and, though she seemed to have succeeded, the flower was not happy and drooped its head and died. Or it would survive for a while and then vanish away. Only one flower was always easy to dig up and always happy when moved. It was a little yellow flower that came every spring. Indeed it seemed grateful to Eve for bringing it into her garden, and, as if to thank her, would put on an extra burst of blossoms as soon as it had settled into its new home. And it would reappear year after year, always coming into bloom earlier and staying in bloom later than its fellows in the forest.

Some of her successes, she had to admit, were accidental. On one occasion she had brought home some twigs that were just coming into leaf and which she thought would look gay in a pot by their bed. But as she had not wanted to go inside just yet, she had pushed them into the ground to keep them fresh. Then Adam had come home rather earlier than usual and she had forgotten about them, so that it was not until many days later that she had rediscovered them; and to her great surprise they were now in fullest leaf. She had pulled one of the twigs out of the ground and found it had grown tiny threads of root. This was another big discovery; for cutting twigs was very much easier than finding seedlings. But she could not persuade every tree to behave in this way.

Their daily life had recently changed. There had been a time when they had found all they had needed within their garden, and they had shared the work of gathering it. But as time went by the garden seemed to be providing less – or was it that they were wanting more? – and so they had ranged further afield. Or rather it was Adam who ranged. Eve preferred to stay nearer home and prepare whatever it was that he brought back from his expeditions. It might be a fruit from some distant tree, or it might be some wild creature, a bird or an animal, that he had pursued and caught.

Then when they were together again he could tell her of his adventures. He liked to do this. He liked boasting of his triumphs and he was proud of his strength and his skill. Eve thought him very brave and very wonderful and she loved listening to him. But it made her feel glad she had not been with him. The forest frightened her. It was so different from her garden.

She stretched herself out on the grass beneath the large tree in whose shade her spring flowers grew in such abundance. Adam would be home very soon now. The sun was low, its rays coming in under the branches of the tree. Soon it would drop behind the hill. There were not many flowers at this time of year. Those still alive were tall, some almost as tall as she was, holding their heads above the surrounding grass. The autumn gales had not yet come to lay them all flat.

A bird cried urgently as it flew low over the tops of the bushes, a black bird shouting its usual evening message. What was it saying? She wished she could understand it. Another bird, little bigger than an insect, flung her a string of defiance at the top of its voice, then popped into a hole in the bank and vanished.

The butterflies that had been so busy all day among the few remaining flowers had gone off to wherever butterflies spend the night. Only the small blue ones could now be seen. For they slept, wings folded above their bodies, clinging to the tops of the tallest grasses. Before going inside with Adam on his return, she liked to count them on her fingers and then wish them all goodnight.

Eve looked up into the branches of the tree. This was her favourite tree. It was large and spreading. The lowest branches were within reach and it was possible to scramble up into them. From there on the going was easier. The branches above were smaller, making them good to grip, and they were closer together; and soon she could be as high as it was safe to go. Sometimes she would be up in her tree when Adam came home and she could watch him looking for her. Then she would call very gently. 'Adam!' He would hear her and look round, searching. Where was she? 'Adam. Look upwards.' Ah, there she was. Their eyes would meet and they would laugh.

She had another reason for liking this particular tree: in the spring it was covered with flowers. Other trees came into flower but none had such magnificent blossoms. The flowers came before the leaves. Clusters of pink buds; then white blossoms; then the petals falling like snow. After that came the leaves to give welcome shade throughout the summer. Finally in the autumn came the fruits, larger by far than the berries on the other trees, large and round and red and shining, like the setting sun on a misty evening.

They were bright red now and they were beginning to fall. Thump! One landed close behind her. She raked through the grass with her fingers and came upon a little cluster of them huddled together. She hardly knew which were the more beautiful, the white flowers in the spring or the red fruits in the autumn. The smaller birds and insects seemed to prefer the flowers, while the larger birds preferred the fruits.

She was reclining on her elbow holding one of the fruits in her hand. It fitted snugly into her palm and she enjoyed the sensation of holding it. She gazed at it thoughtfully. Once, a long time ago, when she was up in the tree scrambling from branch to branch, daring herself to go a little higher, she had picked one of these fruits and had nibbled it, pretending that she was a bird. It was hard and it tasted very sharp and unpleasant and it made her mouth feel dry. She had told Adam and he had been very angry and had said that the Lord God had forbidden them to eat the fruit from that particular tree. She must never do it again. 'Not even when they are red?' she had asked. 'That is when the birds eat them. May we not eat them too? Are they not good for us?' But he had answered only that it was forbidden.

61

Eve looked again at the apple in her hand. For indeed it was an apple. She pressed it with her thumb. It was soft and her pressure left a small dent. She noticed a place where the skin was missing and the flesh was mottled brown and white. A bird had found it first. She held it up to the sky: red against blue. She tried holding it up against the sun, but the sun dazzled her. She balanced it on her thigh. Then she picked it up once more, holding it by the stalk as the tree had held it and swinging it to and fro.

Then at last a voice in her ear said 'Eat it!' and she ate.

It was the voice of the serpent that had spoken. She knew at once that she had been tempted, that she had succumbed and had done something that one day she might bitterly regret. All this she knew but at the same time she was overwhelmed by the taste of the apple she had eaten. It was like nothing she had ever eaten before. Its white flesh was firm, yet where her teeth had entered, the juice had spurted and flowed over her tongue. It was sweet yet also sour, a perfect blend of the two, to which, after she had swallowed, was added a very slight hint of bitterness. She ate it all without a pause, not even to reject the pips and core. And as she finished the last mouthful she caught sight of Adam coming up the path towards her.

There was still a chance. She could have kept her secret to herself. But the experience had been so wonderful that the discovery had to be shared.

Poor Adam! The sack he was carrying had little in it. He had had an unsuccessful day and he was hot and tired and very thirsty and in a bad humour. With scarcely a thought he seized the apple that Eve held out to him and devoured it ravenously. Then, without speaking, he searched the grass and found another and ate it slowly, deliberately and – it seemed to Eve – almost defiantly.

Then he sat silent, staring straight ahead of him.

Eve felt frightened. 'They are so good,' she said in a whisper. 'It cannot be wrong to eat them ... Adam, it *cannot* be wrong.'

He looked at her. He too seemed suddenly afraid.

63

'Adam, come closer to me.' And she held out her hand to him. But he continued to sit apart and stare at her.

'What are you thinking?' But he only shook his head.

The sun had gone behind the hill and a sudden needle of wind pricked her and made her shiver.

She stood up. 'Let's go in now. It's getting cold and you are hungry.'

'No,' said Adam. 'Not yet. I must think.'

He rose slowly to his feet and looked up into the tree.

'So many,' he said, almost as if he regretted their abundance.

'They will not harm us?' asked Eve, going towards him. 'They are not poisonous?'

Poisonous? It was a strange word.

'No,' he replied. 'They are not poisonous. That I now know.'

'You thought they were? That was why we couldn't eat them?' she asked, hoping he might say 'Yes'. But he only shook his head again.

'Look,' he said. He emptied his sack on the ground and a few small green fruits rolled out. They too were apples – of a kind. 'That's all there were. That's all I could find. There were enough on the tree when I last went, but they were not ripe. Today they were all gone – all but these few.'

'Who took them?'

'How should I know? I wasn't there to watch . . . If only all our food grew *here* where we *could* watch it and protect it and tend it . . . Out there it's so scattered. . . .'

And then quite suddenly the idea came to him.

In later years, as she listened to Adam telling his story to his descendants – listening in silence as became a dutiful wife – it would make Eve smile to herself that somehow he always forgot to mention that it was *she* who had first discovered the possibility of digging plants out of the ground and moving them to another place, and *she* who discovered that trees and bushes could sometimes be persuaded to grow where you wanted them to grow by pushing little bits of them into the earth. Yes, of course, it needed a clever, practical man like Adam to make use of her discovery, to see that if flowers could

64

be moved so too could food plants. And so too, quite possibly, could animals. And of course it was Adam's idea that led to the great change in their lives. No. Even that was not quite true. For this change would have occurred in any case, as a result of her eating the apple. If she had never been tempted, never disobeyed, would Adam's wonderful idea have had such consequences? How complicated it all was!

Eve never managed to puzzle it out to her complete satisfaction. Better, therefore, to let Adam tell the story in his own way. The thing had happened whatever might have been its causes and origins and whoever might fairly claim the credit – or take the blame – and whether it was chance or the deep workings of inevitability that lay at the back of it all.

This at least was certain: they had spent the rest of that evening in long discussion, the red apples and the green apples lying side by side on the ground quite forgotten.

'Just think,' said Adam, 'how much easier it would be if *all* our food grew here where I could look after it.'

'It did once, you remember.'

'It could again. I'd have to get rid of everything we didn't need: all the things we can't eat.'

'You can't eat my flowers,' said Eve defensively. 'Would you get rid of them? They're not useful but they are pretty . . . At least I think so.'

'Food must come first,' said Adam firmly.

He walked a little way and Eve hurried after him. It was a wonderful idea but somehow it frightened her. She had been so happy the way things were, even though in winter they had often gone hungry. It had been hard for Adam, it is true. But he had seemed contented. He enjoyed his expeditions into the forest and his adventures there. He enjoyed his hunting. Would he not miss this if he were now to spend all his time in the garden? And what would *she* do? Would he want her to help him? She wondered if she would be allowed to keep her own little corner the way she liked it.

'Please, Adam. This bit here, where my yellow flowers grow and where it is so pleasant to sit. You could sit here too after

you had done your work. You'd have more time for sitting. . . . I like just being with them,' she added, almost to herself. 'Not *doing* anything – though I may perhaps pick a few and bring them inside. Not even looking at them – though I sometimes like to get very close to them and stare deep into their hearts. Just being with them: feeling that they and I are sharing something together, though I don't know what it is. Perhaps it's the world we share, or our small bit of it. And then if I sit still perhaps I will see a fly or some other tiny creature, and he too will come into my world and share it with me.'

Adam, who hadn't been listening, didn't answer. His mind was so full of his wonderful new idea, this idea of not taking the world as it was but of making it the way you wanted it to be. Already in imagination he was digging at the grass, clearing the soil, cutting and burning, making all ready for the new plants he would be bringing in from the forest. Why had he never thought of doing this before? The first thing for Eve to do would be to collect all the fallen apples before the birds got them. Of course it would all take time, years perhaps. He would have to experiment, find out which things were easiest to move and what was the best way of moving them.

He climbed the hill. Yes, Eve had certainly made it very pleasant up here. He came to a tree he did not remember having seen before, a tree now heavy with strangely-coloured fruit. The tree was large and the fruit out of reach. Perhaps that was why Eve had never picked them. He didn't think they had been forbidden.

As he stood looking up into the branches Eve came and joined him.

'It's pretty,' she said. 'Especially in the spring. But I don't think you can eat them.'

'I'd like to try one,' he answered. 'We didn't know about the apples until we had tried them.'

'Not now,' said Eve. 'We've done enough for one day. I'll see if I can reach you one tomorrow.'

She smiled, a little sadly, and put an arm round his waist.

2

The Lord God said, 'The man has become
like one of us knowing good from evil.
What if he now reaches out his hand and
takes fruit from the tree of life also, eats it
and lives for ever?'

So to the man he said: 'You have listened
to your wife and have eaten from the tree
which I forbade you. So now with labour
must you win your food all the rest of your
life.'

And to the woman he said: 'From hence
forward your husband shall rule over you.'

And he drove them out of the Garden.

Then Adam lay with his wife and she
conceived and gave birth to Cain; and
afterwards she had another child, his
brother Abel.

Abel became a shepherd and Cain a tiller
of the soil.

THE boys had been fighting again. It seemed to Eve they were always fighting – and about such little things. They would be working together happily, seemingly the best of friends, and then one would say something, and the other would take offence . . . and they would be off. They were so prickly, so easily offended, each so jealous of the other's achievements. She had talked about it to Adam but, strangely, it didn't seem to worry him. 'A little competition does them good,' he had laughed. 'That's the way to get on.' And certainly they had got on since leaving Eden. Eve couldn't deny that.

Yes, they had left: the Lord God had decreed it. Eve was sad to go. She had loved it there. Adam was less sad. He could see that the garden was not really suitable. It was too confined, too perfect. It would have been wrong to try and change it: here he agreed with Eve. What he needed was a wilderness that he could clear and shape and make exactly as he wanted it to be. The place they had come to suited him perfectly.

Adam was immensely proud of what he had done in the short time they had been here. 'Come and look,' he would say to Eve when the day's work was over. And they would go out together and he would show her and she would admire; and then he would tell her of his plans. He was always so full of plans, of dreams for the future: new tools he was experimenting with, new crops he hoped to plant, new ways of protecting his stock, new places where he might extend his land.

His stock, *his* crops, *his* land. This was the great difference since they had left Eden. There they had been hunters. Now they were farmers. Or rather Adam was a farmer and so were the boys. It was man's work. She was . . . What? A farmer's wife, she supposed. 'His', 'Ours', 'Mine'. These were words they had scarcely used in the old days. In the forest things didn't belong to you. They didn't belong to anybody. They were just there and you took what you wanted, what you could catch or what you could find. When you had caught it and brought it home, then of course it was yours. Who else could it belong to? And then you ate it and that made it still more yours. But here on the farm there was, it seemed, a need to claim ownership, and so you said, 'This is mine.' You said it confidently, proudly. But sometimes you said it challengingly, as if expecting someone to dispute it. This too she had mentioned to Adam; for it made her uneasy, this new relationship with the world around them. But again Adam had laughed at her fears. 'Weren't they "your" flowers that you used to dig up and bring back to "your" garden?' And she had to admit that this was partly true.

The great difference, she decided, was that when they had been hunters they had lived from day to day – or very nearly. When they had wanted something, they had gone out and found it and then straight away they had used it. Sometimes, it is true, they had watched fruit ripening and had said to each other, 'Next week we will come and pick it.' But they had never thought of the fruit as belonging to them until it had been gathered and brought home. They had not laid claim to it while it was still green. And if, in the interval, some other creature took it – well – they would probably find more elsewhere. But now that they were farmers Adam worked as much for the future as for the present. Reaping: that was for the present; but sowing: that was for the future. And there was a long and anxious period between the two when he had to protect his unfinished work until the fruits of his labour could be realised.

Nor was that the only difference. Because in Eden they had

lived from day to day, eating the food they had brought home, burning the fuel they had gathered, there had been little left over at the end of the year to show for the year's work. But now each day something of the day's work survived and was added to what had survived from the previous day, and this brought steady change, steady progress. Eve knew that Adam found this immensely satisfying and that it gave him tremendous pleasure to go out first thing in the morning and stand and survey what he had done the day before, what he had achieved to date. The Lord God when he had made the world had doubtless felt the same. He had looked on his work and seen that it was good. Day by day he had added to it, and day by day it had become more perfect.

That was the great blessing of their new life; and even though it was a blessing that fell mainly upon Adam and the boys, Eve was grateful for it. It made Adam so happy, so proud of what he had done, so eager for Eve's admiration, so full of plans. He used to say that before going to sleep he would lie awake and in his head dream, minute by minute, his next day's tasks. He said that this not only doubled the pleasure, but that in his dreaming he could experiment and so discover the best way of doing things.

This made Eve smile. 'How you do love work!' Well, if he enjoyed it, there could be no harm in it. And certainly they were warmer and better fed than they had ever been. Yes, here indeed was a blessing – despite the quarrelling that it so often seemed to provoke. But alongside it went something that distressed her.

In the old days they had sought what they had wanted where it was to be found. They had gone hunting. Not necessarily together, of course, for Adam liked to penetrate deep into the forest where the wild animals lived. He loved these expeditions, revelling in the chase, exulting in his triumph when with a well-hurled spear he had brought down his quarry. Eve's arms were not made for throwing nor were her legs made for running. And though she was happy to cook what was already dead, she disliked killing and she disliked even more to see creatures die.

Yet she too in her way was a hunter. Her expeditions took her only to the fringe of the forest. Here she would hunt for berries and nuts and leaves and the eggs of birds. She knew – it seemed she had always known – where these things were to be found. Not all plants were good to eat of course. You had to know what you were looking for. Eve knew. It didn't matter to her that there were a lot of other things that she was not looking for. She let them be.

But now it did matter. Now it seemed there were bad things as well as good, and the bad things could not be ignored. They had to be fought and destroyed. As hunters they needed to know only what was good. As a farmer Adam had to know also what was bad.

Eve disliked the idea that something could be bad, a bird or an insect or an animal or a plant with a pretty flower. And she disliked the idea of destroying something because it was bad. You could kill a thing if you were going to use it in some way: you could kill it for its goodness. But it was altogether different to kill it because you did *not* want it.

Adam couldn't see this. 'Weeds and pests,' he had said. (And the very words were new: there had been no weeds or pests either in the forest or in the garden.) 'Weeds and pests have to be destroyed if we want anything to eat. I'm not going to labour day after day clearing the soil, ploughing and sowing, only to watch the birds come down and help themselves to my corn when it's ripe. I'm not working for them. I'm working for us.'

He was quite right of course. It was *his* corn from the moment the seed was in the ground. His ground. His corn. But it was not just that. For Eve had noticed – and this greatly troubled her – that he was no reluctant fighter, doing what he had to do because he had to do it. On the contrary, he enjoyed it. He relished it. Sometimes, in the old days, when he had come home with an animal and Eve had praised him, he had seemed dissatisfied. Eve, puzzled, had asked him what was wrong and he had given the curious reason that he had caught it too easily. It had never worried Eve that she had found her plants too easily. Quite the reverse! But Adam liked what he called 'a

good chase'. He would swear that the meat from a creature that had 'put up a good fight' tasted the sweetest – though Eve herself could never detect any difference.

Adam liked a fight not just for the meal that followed it but for the pleasure of testing his skill and his strength against 'a worthy adversary'. He welcomed the challenge and he exulted in the victory. Though he had never admitted as much, Eve believed that there were occasions when, in the heat of the chase, intoxicated with success, he had killed more creatures than he had been able to carry home and had left the others where they had fallen.

So perhaps it was not altogether surprising that he should now welcome – yes, actually welcome – the attacks that were made on his crops and his sheep. They challenged his authority. They tested his skills. They brought him the 'victories' that so elated him. But Eve, out walking and coming across the body of a dead wolf, or a heap of withered plants – 'weeds' she supposed – would be saddened.

This difference between them explained why, though she had enjoyed her share of the hunting, she could never be a farmer. She was grateful to the Lord God for her days in Eden. She herself could have stayed there for ever. But perhaps for Adam's sake they had to leave. And so perhaps the greatest gift the Lord God could have given them when the time came for their departure lay within the apple they had eaten: a knowledge of good *and evil*. For if there would be enemies opposing their new way of life, surely they needed to know them.

At the time it had puzzled her that God should have said to Adam, 'With labour shall you win your food.' For she had imagined that, once they had found and made a new home for themselves, life would be easier. She had been wrong. It was harder. Yet was it not also in some ways better, more rewarding?

She had been puzzled, too, that God had said to her that Adam would rule over her; for in the Garden neither had wished to 'rule over' the other. This too she could now under-

stand. It was a man's world they had entered, a world in which
his love of risk, of adventure and of success, of challenge, of
struggle and of victory would find all the opportunities it
needed – until in the end, she supposed, he would be lord of the
entire world and every plant and every animal that he had
allowed to survive would owe him allegiance.

Eve sighed. It was harvest time. The autumn always made
her sad, though for Adam and the boys it was the culmination
of the year's work, a time of triumph and of celebration. They
would celebrate as they always did, with a feast. Abel would
bring a lamb, Cain some corn. It was good that they had agreed
to divide the work in this way, Abel looking after the sheep,
Cain the crops. It helped to keep them apart and so gave them
less cause to quarrel with each other.

She heard their voices and the sound of their footsteps and
went outside to greet them.

3

Cain said to his brother, 'Let us go into the open country.' And while he was there he attacked his brother and murdered him.

Then Adam lay with his wife again and she bore a son and named him Seth.

THE avenue was Adam's pride. He had begun planting it when Seth had been born. He had started it at their doorstep and each year he had added a few trees to it, carrying it forwards, absolutely straight, across the valley towards the wild country that at that time lay at the far end. The trees had come from a nearby forest. Adam had found them and dug them up, beeches mostly, but also an occasional oak. They had been waist high when he had moved them and for several years they had not grown at all. In the spring new leaves had come; in the autumn they had turned brown and the late winter gales had finally blown them away just as the new buds were fattening up. The leaves of the oak were a different shape from those of the beech but apart from that there was little to distinguish the one from the other.

Then one year, in the early summer, they noticed a change. New shoots, the length of a hand, had appeared almost overnight on the first trees Adam had planted. Thereafter, each year, as he added to his avenue, so, following behind him but keeping their distance, another group of the older trees would start to grow; and it was in this annual growth that the different personalities of the two kinds of tree first emerged.

In this they were like human children which, all babies at first, later separate into boys and girls. So in their annual growth beeches became feminine, oaks masculine. Eve would refer to them as 'your boys' and 'my girls'.

'Look at your boys now,' she would say. 'Bristling with a hundred spears. Don't they frighten you?' There was indeed something aggressive about the way the young oaks grew, their new shoots, straight as arrows, stabbing in all directions. How different were the beeches, whose delicate new growth, like the waters of a fountain, arched up, curved over and drooped towards the ground. There they hung, graceful and modest, for over a month, then slowly stiffened and straightened until they were pointing skywards.

The avenue marked a new beginning in their lives. For, with Abel's death and Cain's departure, Adam's first high hopes of success had crashed to the ground. It was not just the sudden and tragic loss of two children. Children come and go. This they could have borne. What frightened them was the effect on their surroundings.

If in Eden there had suddenly been two mouths fewer there would have been more food for the two that survived. But in their new life it was the opposite. With Cain and Abel gone, there was not more to eat but less – alarmingly less. Over the years the three men had pushed forward the boundaries of their land, bringing more and more of the wild country under cultivation.

Adam had imagined that, where he had fought and defeated the enemy, he would remain for ever the undisputed victor. It had not occurred to him that the wilderness, now held at bay only by himself, would so fiercely fight back and so quickly recapture lost territory.

Now more than ever did he appreciate the truth of the Lord God's words: 'With labour shall you win your food.' The thorns and the thistles, more savage than he had ever known them before, were all around him. Eve had been near to despair and had begged Adam to return to Eden so that they might throw themselves on the mercy of the Lord God and beg to be readmitted. But Adam, proud and determined, refused to surrender. He decided how much land he would need for the two of them, which were the most convenient pastures, which soil was the most fertile, and this he defended, driving in stakes and piling up a rampart of earth and stones to form a perimeter defence. The rest he abandoned.

Ten years after Seth's arrival he was able once more to push forward and regain a little of what he had lost. More sons and daughters quickly followed, and all, as they grew up, moved away across the plain, clearing the wilderness and establishing farmsteads of their own.

Generation after generation the farmsteads moved eastwards, and, as they spread out across the plain, so the techniques of agriculture improved. But always there were battles: these were unending. Man having once put his hand to the plough could never again rest.

Adam left the young to their fighting. He had reached middle age. His great battles were now over. He and the rest of nature had come to accept each other's existence, and a truce had been established. He continued to farm but in a smaller, gentler way, a few sheep and a few crops. If extra help were needed, then one or other of his sons would come over to lend a hand.

Eve too had established a truce. For, yes, she too had become a fighter, though a much gentler and more reluctant one than Adam. She did not work in the fields except at harvest time. She and her daughters had enough to do in and around their home, a home which they shared, inevitably, with a host of other creatures.

Some of these had been in residence before she and Adam had arrived and had subsequently adapted themselves to the presence of humans. Others, approving of the alterations being made, had moved in. For there is throughout nature, from the lowliest plants to man himself, a constant coming and going as circumstances change.

Eve did not divide her fellow residents into 'good' and 'evil' but she did give a warmer welcome to some than to others. It was not just that she favoured those plants and animals that she and Adam could eat or that served some other practical purpose. Some creatures she liked simply for themselves, for no better reason than that they seemed to like her and be happy in the company of each other. She came to regard them as part of her family.

Others she liked because she had known them as a child and they had established a special place in her affections. It was soon after the birth of Seth that she had begun to feel this nostalgia for her first garden, and she had tried to introduce some of the flowers that had grown there into her new garden. But she was not always successful. The newcomers were often unhappy. The older residents resented their intrusion. Eve got angry with them and Adam was amused to hear her referring to them as 'weeds'. After a short while the attempt was abandoned.

Thus Eve in her home and Adam in his fields reached in the end a stable relationship with their surroundings. Their arrival had been followed by years in which great changes had occurred. But these changes were now over and a new pattern had replaced the old. Yet though in temperament husband and wife were now much closer than they had been at the start, a difference still remained, a difference which, for better or for worse, was always to distinguish man from woman.

Then came the visit to Jared.

People in those times lived a great deal longer than they do today. Jared was then around sixty and still had another hundred years to wait before his first son was born. Adam was his great-great-great-grandfather and had just reached his five hundredth birthday.

Their journey across the plain was almost the first time they had left their own valley and certainly by far the longest distance they had ever attempted. Travelling outwards they were thus seeing, largely for the first time, a pageant of four hundred years of human progress, and it took them into a land very different from the one they knew so well.

For Adam it was a fascinating experience, passing through a landscape that was perpetually changing, trying to understand the new methods that were being used, the new tools, marvelling at the new buildings where people lived together in such large communities. Eve, though she had a mother's pride in the achievements of her children and her children's children – in the sheer numbers of them that now filled the plain – felt uneasy at what they had done. It was all so frighteningly different.

Where would it end? There had been much to admire certainly, but they had passed a place where something had clearly gone wrong. The landscape was ravaged and naked. Nothing grew there – just tree stumps, bare earth, stagnant pools of water and what looked like the decaying remnants of abandoned buildings now little more than sad heaps of stones.

84

What exactly had happened? The answers she had been given were evasive.

On their return journey the pageant was reversed: they were travelling backwards through time. They were discussing what they had seen and Eve's anxiety about the future was weighing on her. They had again passed the place that had so frightened her on the outward journey and it had frightened her even more seeing it a second time. She was convinced that something evil had happened, and on top of this was a conviction that in some way she had been to blame.

This feeling of guilt had assailed her once before – when Abel had been killed – and it had taken many years to recover from it. Now it assailed her again. For surely all evil, all suffering lay at her door. She had disobeyed the command of the Lord God. It was true that the serpent had tempted her. But the choice had been hers. And not only had she disobeyed; she had persuaded Adam to do likewise. She was thus doubly guilty. That single act of disobedience had totally changed the pattern of all their lives. All the sorrows of the world had their origin in what she had done.

'It's all my fault,' she cried.

'What is?' said Adam. Their thoughts had diverged since last they had spoken to each other.

'Evil,' said Eve simply.

'Then Good too,' answered Adam. 'We saw plenty of that.'

But Eve was not so easily consoled and Adam tried another argument.

'You remember the wound on Jared's hand that you helped to wash, and how he told us it came from a tool he had been using? He showed me that tool. He had made it himself. It was a wonderful thing. Sharper and better than anything I have ever been able to make. Now tell me, was that tool evil to have injured the hand that held it? Or was Jared wicked to have invented it? If you invent tools that make work easier, you must accept the risk that they can do greater damage.'

'I don't see what that has to do with disobedience,' Eve said.

Adam was silent for a little. Then he tried again.

'When Seth was a child we told him that, though he might go down to the stream, he must never cross over to the other side unless he was with one of us. We made that rule, not because there were greater dangers on the far side of the stream, nor because there was any particular risk that he might slip and drown in trying to get across, but simply because it made it easier for us to look after him. If we had allowed him his freedom to wander where he pleased, he might well have wandered too far and got lost or met with some accident and we might never have found him. I chose the stream as his limit for no other reason than that it made a clear boundary between what was permitted and what was forbidden. If he chose to cross, I would punish him: that he knew.

'But I knew – and he didn't – that one day he *would* cross. *And I would be glad.* I would be glad because it would prove that he was no longer a child dependent upon his father for protection but a man dependent only upon himself. I could have said, "Today you are a man. Now you have my permission." But I preferred him to make the discovery for himself. I preferred that the time and the decision should be his, not mine. You do not become a man because your father says you are one, but because you feel yourself to be one.

'That is how it was with Seth, and it was exactly the same with us when we were children and lived in Eden, and the Lord God was our father. He provided for us. Our food was there, all around us, and we helped ourselves to it, while he watched over us. Then when we were strong enough to be independent of him, we proved it to him by breaking his command. And the apple which had been forbidden to us when we were children became his great gift to us, the gift that enabled us to survive on our own.'

'But I never wanted to leave my garden,' cried Eve. 'That wasn't why I ate the apple. It was . . . I don't know . . . curiosity.'

'Nor, I think, did Seth want to leave home. But he proved to me that he was ready to go, and so I sent him away. It is right for children to leave home when they are grown up. That was our mistake with Cain and Abel: we allowed them to stay.'

'It is good of you, dear Adam, to excuse me. And perhaps the Lord God excuses me too. But I fear others may not do so. They will see it differently.'

'If things go right our children will, of course, give themselves the credit. If they go wrong they will look for others to blame. Yes, they will certainly blame us.'

They walked on in silence.

After a while Eve said: 'I was very frightened at first. Frightened of you. Did you know?'

'There were times when I was a bit frightened of myself,' answered Adam with a laugh.

'You became so different; so . . . so . . .' She sought in vain for the word. 'I didn't like that fighting. All that killing. We seemed to have so many enemies and you were so fierce.'

'I had to be,' said Adam. 'We couldn't have survived any other way.'

'I'm glad it's over now. But they are still fighting up there – Jared and the others. Does the great plain stretch for ever or does it come to an end? What happens when they reach the end? What happens on the other side?'

Adam shook his head. He had never thought of such a possibility.

They were nearing home now. The landscape was becoming more familiar. The late winter sun was level with their eyes, orange and no longer dazzling. Their elongated shadows trailed behind them. It had suddenly turned cold after a day of rare warmth. Soon afterwards the track went downhill. They were entering their valley at last and the sun, having guided them across the plain, its duty done, now slipped quietly behind the far horizon.

The valley beneath them lay in shadow, a monochrome of black and grey, but the sky was still alive with colour from deepest crimsons to palest greens. As they made their way down the hill so, one by one, the valley trees seemed to rise up out of the darkness to greet their return. One by one they thrust their leafless heads through the rim of the sleeping world, and

as they moved upwards into the sky so they caught in the network of their branches a million fragments of colour, a shoal of rubies and emeralds and amethysts and sapphires. Many thousands of years later men would celebrate this evening flowering of winter trees in the stained glass windows of their churches. But though they were able to capture the colours, the individual personalities of the trees themselves eluded them.

These were Adam's trees. He had planted them, every one. He knew them as he knew his own children. Indeed they were his children. And this was how he and Eve liked best to see them, naked against the winter's sky.

First to salute them was the oak with the straight trunk and the round head that stood where the track began to level out; and soon afterwards came two more solitary oaks.

'Rough old oaks,' said Eve. 'Their heads are as bristly as your beard.'

'They are men,' said Adam. 'They are my sons.'

'And the beeches are our daughters.'

Adam smiled. 'Their trunks are smooth like the body of a woman. Their branches are like a woman's arms; and their heads have a woman's hair, as fine and soft as the wind itself. They are indeed our daughters.'

'They are like us,' said Eve, 'and yet they are the opposite of us. For in winter when we need clothes to keep warm they are naked, and in the summer when we are naked they are clothed.'

'I like them naked best,' said Adam. 'I like you naked best, too. You are you when you are naked. I can see you and touch you and know you. When the trees are clothed in their leaves I can pick a leaf and say what tree it belongs to, but the leaf will tell me nothing of the nature of the tree. It is the same with clothes; they tell us who we are but not what we are.'

A group of trees, half a dozen clustering together on a little hillock, rose against the sky.

'Look at those oaks,' said Eve. 'Aren't they just like men! Six men having an argument, shouting at each other, elbowing each other, threatening each other. Look how their branches twist and stab, how they fight each other and hurt each other. Poor things! They are wounded trees.'

'Yet they survive,' said Adam, 'wounded or not.'

Another group came into view.

'There! See what a difference,' cried Eve. 'My girls. So close to each other, so happy to be close. Each one perfect, its branches slipping through the branches of its neighbours. No fighting. Just peace and happiness.'

They had reached the avenue now and walked more slowly, arm in arm. It was darker here. The great smooth round columns of the beeches rose on either hand, one behind the other, evenly spaced, stretching away ahead of them. High above their heads each column opened out into its branches, branches that arched up and over, meeting and crossing those of its partner on the opposite side of the track and those of its neighbours on the same side.

Eve held up her arms and arched the palms of her hands towards each other so that her finger tips met and crossed.

'Look. They do it like this.' It was the attitude of prayer.

'When you planted them, did you mean it to be like this? Did you know they would grow this way and make a canopy over our heads?'

'No,' said Adam. 'They were forest trees growing wild when I found them. Trees don't grow in straight lines in the forest. I dug them up and planted them here, two and two, exactly spaced, flanking a path that was as straight as I could make it. I did it that way to show that they were now my trees growing on my land.'

'And that you were their Lord and Master?'

'Yes, and that I was their Lord and Master.'

'Are you still their Lord and Master?'

'They are taller and stronger than I am now. I think perhaps I have given them their freedom, though happily they are reluctant to leave me. I shan't drive them away.'

They had reached the end of the avenue. One solitary tree now filled the sky. It stood quite alone. It was immensely large, towering up into the sky, yet stretching its branches out

horizontally on either side to give it a breadth that was greater even than its great height. This enormous head was carried on a trunk as broad almost as it was tall. It was a giant oak.

'Adam's Oak,' said Eve. 'No mightier tree will the world ever know.'

And she touched its rough bark with her hands and knelt at its foot and rested her head against its trunk and wept.

4

After the birth of Seth Adam lived eight hundred years, and had other sons and daughters. He lived in all nine hundred and thirty years, and then he died.

When the Lord saw that man had done much evil on earth and and that his thoughts and inclinations were always evil, and that the whole world was corrupt and full of violence, he was sorry that he had made man on earth, and he was grieved at heart. He said, 'This race of men whom I have created, I will wipe them off the face of the earth.'

EVE took her largest container and went down to the stream, to the place where Adam had wedged a tree trunk between the banks and filled behind with rocks and earth to make a miniature waterfall. Behind this was a pool where, even in the driest weather, the water was always deep. Here she dipped. Then she carried her burden up the hillside.

She lived alone now. Adam had been dead many years, and the land that lay on the far side of the stream was now farmed by others.

It was midsummer. The winter had been unusually wet, the spring unusually dry. The sun shone from a cloudless sky and had been doing so day after day for an unusually long time.

Eve loved all weathers and all seasons. They were part of the living world, and the to-and-fro movement between them – from darkness to light, from new moon to full moon, from winter to summer, from east wind to west wind, from gale to calm, from rain to sunshine, from frost to thaw – was the world's breathing and showed that it was alive and in good health.

Only when the rhythm became erratic, when the world drew its breath in great spasms like a person who is ill, did she become afraid. And only when she was afraid did she begin to think of the weather as cruel.

Although there is no precise moment when the sun's kindly smile becomes a smile of cruelty, there may well be a precise moment when one becomes aware of such a change. For Eve this moment was the day she carried the water up the hillside to her grove of trees to offer it to the three young saplings she had planted there in the spring.

Eve's grove was like Adam's avenue in that it expressed, whether consciously or not, her attitude towards the living world. In later years men were to express themselves in timber and stone. She and Adam did so in trees. But whereas Adam had planted his beeches evenly spaced in two straight lines – to show, as he used to say, whose trees they were – Eve planted her grove in the more casual way that the trees themselves seemed to prefer. She had begun planting soon after Adam's death and had continued intermittently ever since: oak and ash and beech and hazel mainly, but also occasionally hawthorn and birch and field maple. The three new saplings were hawthorns.

Eve seldom visited her grove in the height of summer. She preferred it in the winter, when the trees rose naked from the naked earth, and in the spring, when the flowers made patches of colour between the trees, yellow first, then blue and finally pink. But after that came a sudden wild upsurge of green that swamped the flowers, and at that season she preferred to sit by the stream where the sheep grazed and the grass was short.

There had been no rain for so long that she had begun to fear for her three hawthorns. Newly-planted trees dislike a drought. She had been up the hill that morning to search for them, fighting her way through head-high bracken to reach them. They were indeed dry. Their leaves were hanging limply and some had already turned yellow. She was returning now with the water they so badly needed.

She began to pour it round the base of the first tree. She had imagined that because the soil here was so dry and powdery, so obviously thirsty, it would swallow the water at a gulp, and she was disconcerted to find that, so far from soaking in, it merely rolled off down the slope. She stopped pouring at once, put down her container and loosened the soil with her fingers. Then she poured again, and again the water rolled away. So she found a stick and with its help she scooped out a hollow behind the stem of the tree and brought the earth forward to form a rampart in front. The rest of her water she now poured into this hollow until it was level with the top of her rampart. Then she went down the hill to collect more water.

On her return she found the pool as deep as ever. She visited the other two trees and prepared them in the same way, excavating the soil at the back and bringing it to the front. Then she filled both hollows with water.

After a rest, for it was hot and wearying work, she visited the stream for the third time. She thought she might manage six journeys a day – two for each tree – and she hoped this might be enough to keep them alive until the rain came.

But the three water levels were unchanged. She went to the first tree, tried pouring a little more and for a moment thought it was soaking in. Then she noticed a thin trickle snaking its way through the grass between her feet. She thrust her hand down into the water and scrabbled with her fingers into the soil. She jabbed with her stick to loosen the stones. Some fragments of dust rose to the surface and were joined a moment afterwards by a tiny insect. The insect dented the surface of the water. Its legs raced but to no effect. Eve watched its futile efforts. The water was still gently girating from her work with the stick, and the insect, caught in the movement, circled the pool.

'Poor creature,' said Eve. 'My efforts are as little welcome to you as they are to my tree.' And she dipped her finger in and drew it up and it sat on her finger tip encased in a drop of water. She shook her finger and the insect vanished.

That for Eve was the day the drought began, the day the kindly sun turned cruel. Its cruelty was not directed against her personally. She had plenty to eat and plenty to drink. If she was too hot she could move into the shade or bathe herself in the stream. What pained her was the suffering she saw or imagined she saw in the other creatures, particularly the suffering of the earth itself.

To Eve the earth had always seemed alive, the living home of countless living plants and animals. Lying upon it she could feel it holding her up, powerful and reassuring beneath her body. Pressing her hands against it she could feel the living earth press back. She would explore it and caress it with her fingers. She would press her face into it and inhale its living breath.

But now and in the days that followed it hurt her to look at it, so different had it become, like a friend greatly changed through illness. It glared back at her as if it had never known her, as if it cared nothing for her, grim and unloving, locked in its own private torment.

She continued to water her three trees. A single container a day shared between them was all she could persuade them to drink, and she doubted very much whether it would be enough. There was so little she could do for the suffering earth, but to do nothing was worse. Each day she carried her water up the hillside and poured it. It became a daily ritual, a symbolic gesture that expressed her feelings of love and faith; and she found it strangely satisfying.

Then one afternoon she noticed a change. A tenseness seemed to grip the world. There were sudden rustlings, sudden puffs of wind. Birds flew from tree to tree. The sheep were unusually noisy. Towards evening the sky became slashed and streaked and smeared with strange patterns of cloud. Soon afterwards it grew very dark.

Then came the noise of the approaching storm. The wind had dropped. The waiting world held its breath in silence, and so the first sounds came from far away, a gentle hissing that grew steadily louder and louder, increasing to a roar that reached its climax with a great crash as giant hailstones hurtled out of the pitch black sky and battered the earth all round her. Eve quickly got under cover and the noise on the roof over her head was deafening.

The hailstorm died away and was followed by a steady torrent of rain. She ventured outside again and stood naked with her arms stretched up towards the sky. The rain stung her body and soaked her and washed the salt sweat from her skin. She threw back her head and shut her eyes and opened her mouth and let the rain beat upon her teeth and upon her tongue. There was so much rain that it drowned the air, making it hard to breathe. All around her came a steady roar as the water hit the earth and flattened it into submission. She stood thus, exulting, then went inside.

The rain was streaming through the roof and the floor was awash. In the darkness she sought her bed and lay down and covered herself over to wait for daylight. She was cold. She had almost forgotten what it was like to feel cold and she enjoyed the sensation. Then, pulling her coverings close over her body and over her head, she enjoyed the sensation of returning warmth. She lay awake listening to the noises that were all around her – the sudden buffetings of the wind, the creakings from the roof, the periodic slitherings and thumpings and drippings and splashings and cascadings as more and more of the roof surrendered to the storm. And twice she heard from afar a long-drawn rending, tearing, splintering crash as some hard-pressed tree succumbed to the combined onslaught of wind and water.

As soon as a faint grey daylight returned to the world she got up and went outside. Adam had built well. Only the roof had suffered; and though torrents of water were spouting from the hillside, the wall that encircled their home had not been breached. Beyond it, however, was desolation: the grass flattened, trees with their branches weighed to the ground with water, leaves and broken twigs everywhere, water and earth and stones swirling and leaping down the hillside, a strong sweet smell of sap in the air, the rain as heavy as ever.

Back under cover again she noticed that as the rain dried on her body the hairs on her skin became dark brown. When she wiped herself there remained a muddy smear.

During the day the rain slackened a little, its first fury spent, and she was able to make some repairs and salvage her belongings. The following day she ventured to the stream. The bridge had vanished and she doubted if she could now get safely across.

As she stood there, something large and white came bounding down on the flood. It was a sheep. It passed beyond her reach. But even if it had been nearer she could never have checked its wild progress. And in any case it was dead.

Closer to the bank where the water travelled more slowly came a mole. It was paddling frantically, like the tiny insect she had rescued when she had been giving water to the trees, and as the eddies caught it and turned it now this way, now that, so its blind efforts would be directed sometimes towards, sometimes away from the shore. Eve reached out a hand but it eluded her and went spinning on its way.

A sheep and a mole. She wondered what had become of the people.

When she looked outside the next day she was alarmed to find that the stream had become a broad lake whose nearer shore was already climbing the hillside towards her and whose further shore was scarcely visible through the driving rain. As she stood there looking over her wall she saw a figure come down to the water's edge on the far side and appear to be staring in her direction. She waved and shouted. The figure saw her and waved back but no sound reached her.

They waved to each other for a while and Eve shouted that she was all right. But the rain drowned her words and the wind swept the fragments away. There was nothing more they could do. The water divided them and there was no safe way across. Soon afterwards, with a final wave, the figure turned and departed.

The following day the water was so close that Eve decided she must retreat. Behind her rose the mountains. These were the mountains through which she and Adam had journeyed many hundreds of years ago when they had been driven out of Eden. They had crossed the mountains and come to the plain on whose edge they had settled and built their home. And while they had been building it – gathering stones and cutting timber and cementing and daubing with mud – they had taken shelter in a cave they had found on the mountainside. It was this cave that Eve now sought; and to her great relief, though nearly blinded by rain and low cloud, she was able to rediscover it. And it was dry and welcoming.

All that day she journeyed back and forth, carrying food and fuel, and by the evening she had moved her entire store. That night she slept well and it was already daylight when she woke. She went to the mouth of the cave and looked out. It was still raining but the cloud had lifted and the air was clearer. She could see further, and from her elevated position there was further to see.

The plain stretched away to the distant horizon. Not since that first time those many years ago had she seen it thus in all its vastness. Then it had been green and inviting. Now – she could scarcely believe what she saw: there was nothing in front of her but an unbroken expanse of water. Not a hilltop, not a treetop, not a solitary sign of life. All had been totally submerged.

At first she was too numbed with shock to be afraid or to consider what it might mean. She returned to her cave, and hardly knowing what she was doing, she set herself to make it habitable and to sort and tidy and arrange her various belongings. She worked vigorously, keeping her back to the outside world, and when darkness came she was exhausted and ready for bed.

That night she slept restlessly, waking frequently, and, as often happens on such occasions, her dreams were vivid and more closely related to her waking thoughts than is usual. She had three dreams and when morning came at last to lighten the entrance to her cave she was able to recall them all.

In her first dream she was looking down on a great expanse of water. The water was brown and turbulent, and froth and debris floated on its surface. As she looked, a small insect rose to the surface and began paddling. It was followed by a mole, also paddling, then by a dead sheep and finally by a man. Insect, mole, sheep and man, one behind the other, three of them struggling, the fourth quietly floating, circled the water in steady procession.

Eve stretched down and tried to reach them but something restrained her. It was a tree. She was caught in the branches of a great tree. Using both hands to grip the branches below her she managed to pull herself down a little way. But by that time the procession had moved out of range.

She then saw that the water was retained along one side by a rampart of loose earth. If she could only reach this and draw her finger across it she could release the flood. Again she set to work to haul herself downwards; and when she thought she was low enough she took a firm grip with her left hand and heaved, and stretched downwards with her right, and her extended finger was just able to touch the earth. With a tremendous effort, pulling with one hand and stretching with the other, she was able to make a small groove across the rampart, and through this the water began to flow.

As it flowed so it widened and deepened the channel and its level began to fall. Eve watched, expecting at any moment to see treetops and hilltops reappear. Eagerly she scanned the receding waters for the first signs of life. Something ruffled the surface of the water and a moment later a brown island appeared and grew, then another and another. Brown, deserted, dead. No grass; only mud and stones. No trees; only tree stumps. No buildings; only little heaps of stones. And no living thing.

The last of the water drained away. Only a few stagnant pools remained. Over the entire surface no living thing was to be seen. And Eve knew then that the flood had not drowned a living world; it had closed the grave over a world already dead. And she should have left it that way.

*   *   *

In her second dream she was on an island and with her were a great crowd of people. There was frantic activity – sounds of hammering and much shouting – and Eve saw that the men were making an enormous boat. When the boat was ready it was hauled down to the water's edge and the water rose up and floated it off. The people gathered around, shouting and singing. Then the men, some carrying long poles of wood and others armed with swords and spears, climbed on board.

Eve tried to ask her neighbours what they were doing, but they seemed not to hear her. She guessed that the boat was to carry them to safety and that when the men were on board the women would follow. 'We must hurry,' she said. 'The water is rising fast.' But again they took no notice of her.

All the men were now in the boat and still the women stood

on the shore, watching, waving and cheering. 'Quick, quick,' shouted Eve in desperation. But no words came out of her mouth. Slowly the boat moved away from the shore. The poles, beating the surface of the water, like the legs of some giant insect, carried it slowly on its way.

As it moved out across the water, Eve saw another boat appear from behind another island. The two boats converged and the shouting and cheering of the women lining the shore rose to a frenzy. Nearer and nearer they drew to each other and then with a tremendous crash they collided. And now there were men everywhere, surging up on deck, hurling themselves at each other, fighting and killing. The boats were breaking to pieces. Men were in the water. Men were clinging to bits of wreckage. And still they fought on.

And still the watching women, in ever greater frenzy, shouted and cheered and leapt up and down. 'Victory! Victory! Victory!' they yelled. And all the time the flood continued to rise. It was round their ankles, round their knees, round their waists. They took no notice. Still they cried, 'Victory! Victory!' until one by one, they lost their footing, slipped into the water and were carried away.

*   *   *

In Eve's third dream she was walking through her beloved valley and it was springtime. She was on her way home and had just reached the avenue. She was alone, but on either side, between the trees, was a vast gathering of people, men and women and children together with many other creatures. And all around her in the air were strange and very wonderful sounds. These sounds, tangible almost as water, swept round her and lifted her up and carried her forward. Slowly and in great splendour and majesty they carried her down the avenue.

At the far end was the giant oak, its small leaves and flower tassels now radiant in yellow-green. They came to the oak and the people and the other creatures were around her and the sounds, ever louder, ever more thrilling, coursed through her entire body and seized her and lifted her up and placed her high in the branches of the oak. She looked down and the people turned their faces up to her, and among them she saw Adam. 'Adam,' she cried, fearing he hadn't noticed her. 'Adam, look upwards.' Their eyes met and they laughed.

For a while she continued to lie stretched out on the bed that she had made for herself, while dream and reality wrestled with each other. Then quite suddenly she saw what she must do. Indeed there was no alternative. She must return to Eden. Just possibly at the far end of the plain (for the plain must surely have an end) there might be survivors who, like herself, were now clinging to the rim of their world. Just possibly some man somewhere would find a way of surviving the flood. But she and they were separated by an ocean of water and neither could ever know of or come to the help of the other. Those others would have to go on to whatever lay on the far side. She could only go back.

So back she would go. Back through the mountains – if she could find her way – back to the forest where Adam had hunted, back to the garden where they had once lived together so happily. There would be no Adam, and she was now very old. But the Lord God might still be there and he might take pity on her and look after her and clothe her and feed her in her old age.

She went to the mouth of her cave and looked out. The rain had slackened but the prospect was infinitely depressing. Yet if she could find no comfort in what she could see, in her ears she could still hear the wonderful sounds that had accompanied her third dream and this gave her both determination and strength.

She ate. Then she prepared herself for her journey, making up a bundle of food, clothing and various implements she thought might be useful.

Finally, turning her back on the waters that had drowned her valley and the plain and all its inhabitants and all that she and

Adam and their descendants had achieved, all the good and all the evil, she set her face to the mountain and began to climb.

She struggled on through the rest of that day until weariness and darkness overtook her. Then she found an overhanging rock and in the slight shelter that it offered she made herself as comfortable as she could. She was wet and cold and her bed was hard. She ate a little of the food she had brought and tried to close her eyes. But that night no sleep came.

The following morning she ate a little more, repacked her bundle and went on her way. The clouds were all round her and the rain streamed down her face. So she let her feet and her instinct be her guides. They guided her well, as, left to themselves, they often do. Towards midday the sky began to lighten and then to brighten and then quite suddenly she was through the cloud and into the sunshine and could see at last what lay ahead of her.

There were two mountain peaks quite near at hand, one on cither side of her, and the skyline joining them hung in a curve. She directed her feet to the lowest point of this curve; and as she approached it and no other skyline appeared beyond it, so her hopes rose that perhaps this was the ridge that separated the two plains. She stumbled up the last few paces, tripped, fell, but was able to look over the top. Yes, indeed it was the top and Eden lay somewhere beneath her. But alas it was totally hidden in dense cloud.

She lay there for some moments, exhausted but triumphant, pressing the ground with her hands and her face while the sun warmed her back and the wind blew through her hair. Then she got to her feet and stretched herself towards the sky. Then she turned and looked behind her, half hoping, perhaps, to see that the flood waters had subsided.

Whatever had happened down there, nothing of it was visible. Cloud lay below her on both sides. But above her the sky was blue, one single expanse of blue arching over her two worlds. The sky reached down to her and was all around her; and she seemed to flow upwards to meet it. Again she stretched her arms into the air. She threw her head back and opened her mouth and filled her lungs; and a new and strange feeling flowed through her body.

She looked around her to find the exact point at which her path, having left the valley she had come from, began its descent into the valley ahead, the highest point in her journey. And there she stood; and once again everything everywhere – past, present and perhaps also future – became a part of her. She and the world became one.

Then she sat and unwrapped her bundle and laid her possessions out to dry. She was reluctant to begin her descent. It was so beautiful up here, so clean and pure. She divided her remaining food into two equal parts and very slowly she ate one of them. Then she lay down to rest.

A little finger of mist crept up the mountainside and chilled her. She opened her eyes. The sun was lower in the sky. She must be on her way.

She retied her bundle, picked up her stick and began her descent. Soon the sun vanished and the mist was once more all around her.

Somewhere along the bottom, out of sight, ran a little river and on the other side was the forest. If she crossed the river and followed the edge of the forest she would eventually come to the garden.

She reached the river in the late afternoon. She had heard it before she had seen it and it had filled her with alarm. The sight of it confirmed her fears, for it was now a broad and angry torrent.

Anxious to get across as quickly as possible, now that she was so near her journey's end, she stepped into the water and moved out over the smooth stones. A few paces from the bank she lost sight of her feet in the brown and foaming water. She grasped her stick in both hands and moved more cautiously, feeling with her stick, using it as a support, and then sliding her feet. The water was not deep but it pulled strongly round her legs and the stones were slippery. Once she nearly lost her balance. After a while she looked back to see how far she had come. Alas, it was only a tiny distance. She returned to the

shore. If she were ever to reach the other side she must choose the best possible place and then abandon her belongings. All that she had brought with her except her stick must be left behind.

She set off downstream and eventually decided on a spot where the very width of the river led her to hope it might also be shallow. She undressed and, taking her stick, moved into the water a second time.

The far bank was lined with trees which were grey and dim in the misty rain. The wind blew and shook their branches. Eve stood knee deep in the water looking across. What a distance had yet to be covered! Suddenly she saw someone on the other side waving to her. It was Adam.

'Adam,' she cried in amazement. 'How did *you* get there?'

A wild surge of hope swept over her. Adam had gone on ahead of her and was waiting for her! Now surely she would get across. If she slipped and fell he would come to her rescue. With new confidence she moved further out and the water tugged at her thighs.

When she looked up again he had vanished. No. There he was, waving still. The wind came and the branches waved more wildly . . . and Adam dissolved. Two moving branches and a tree trunk: that was all it had ever been. For a moment hope was drowned in despair.

But of course it could not have been Adam. Adam was long ago dead . . . Yet perhaps, though he was dead, something of him still lived and was over there waiting for her, calling to her, urging her not to give up. Perhaps he had been trying to point to her the best way across. Which way had he been pointing? She looked up again. The branches waved. That way! That way!

The wind was all about her. The rain stung her face, almost blinding her. The torrent roared. And through it and in it she heard once again the noble music of her third dream, and it lifted her up and sustained her and gave her strength.

'Adam!' she cried out. 'Wait for me. I'm coming!' She threw away her stick and in perfect confidence she turned and faced the water and leant against it, facing upstream and moving sideways.

The water rose and flung its arms around her waist and the great chords of the music crashed in her ears. . . .